THE BEST OF THE BEST

WELCOME to the Best of *Destinies*. For those of you who've been with us all along, there's little to be said; what can we add in an issue that goes from Anderson (his Nebula-nominee "The Ways of Love") to Zelazny by way of some of the best-loved names in the field. With people like Niven, Pohl, Pournelle, and Sheffield waiting in the wings we shouldn't take up your time. Just turn the page and enjoy.

On the other hand, if you haven't had the pleasure of reading *Destinies* issue by issue, then you *do* have a rare treat in store. Frankly, we envy you. We envy that feeling of coming to the end of this book and wishing there were more. Well, there's a subscription form on the very last page, just where you need to see it, just where it can soothe those feelings of desolation and loss. Have no fear—there's more where this came from! Welcome aboard.

TABLE OF CONTENTS

SCIENCE FICTION

Short Stories

GO STARLESS IN THE NIGHT, Roger Zelazny 5
THE PILOT, Joe Haldeman 18
ASSIMILATING OUR CULTURE, THAT'S WHAT
   THEY'RE DOING, Larry Niven 154
OLD WOMAN BY THE ROAD, Gregory Benford 226
DOMINO, DOMINE, Dean Ing 263

Novelets

THE WAYS OF LOVE, Poul Anderson 26
SKYSTALK, Charles Sheffield 163
ANTINOMY, Spider Robinson 277

Novella

SPIRALS, Larry Niven and Jerry Pournelle 66

SCIENCE FACT

NEW BEGINNINGS, J. E. Pournelle 134
Comes the Revolution, Comrades—In a world of five
billion people, only technology can make us free.

HOW TO BUILD A BEANSTALK, Charles Sheffield 196
It will be a bit more difficult than planting a "beanstalk
seed." On the other hand, the treasure doesn't have an
ogre guarding it.

DEFENDING THE THIRD INDUSTRIAL REVOLUTION,
G. Harry Stine 238
Once you have created something valuable, you had
better be able to protect it.

GOOD-BY TO ALL THAT, Frederik Pohl 324
Retrospective insights from the professionals'
professional—the man who does it all.

THE BEST OF

Edited by JAMES BAEN

SF
ace books
A Division of Charter Communications Inc.
A GROSSET & DUNLAP COMPANY
51 Madison Avenue
New York, New York 10010

THE BEST OF DESTINIES

An ACE Book

Interior art by David Egge, Steve Fabian, Fernando Fernandez, Alex Schomburg, E. T. Steadman

First printing: June 1980

Manufactured in the United States of America

GO STARLESS IN THE NIGHT

by Roger Zelazny

Heroism is not a thing
of the body, but of the spirit
—as are its rewards.

Illustrated by E. T. Steadman

Darkness and silence all about, and nothing, nothing, nothing within it.

Me?

The first thought came unbidden, welling up from some black pool. Me? That's all.

Me? he thought. Then, Who? What . . .?

Nothing answered.

Something like panic followed, without the customary physical accompaniments. When this wave had passed, he listened, striving to capture the slightest sound. He realized that he had already given up on seeing.

There was nothing to hear. Not even the smallest noises of life—breathing, heartbeat, the rasping of a tired joint—came to him. It was only then that he realized he lacked all bodily sensations.

But this time he fought the panic. Death? he wondered. A bodiless, dark sentience beyond everything? The stillness . . .

Where? What point in spacetime did he occupy? He would have shaken his head . . .

He recalled that he had been a man—and it seemed that there were memories somewhere that he could not reach. No name answered his summons, no view of his past came to him. Yet he knew that there had been a past. He felt that it lay just below some dim horizon of recall.

He strove for a timeless interval to summon some recollection of what had gone before. Amnesia? Brain damage? Dream? he finally asked himself, after failing to push beyond a certain feeling of lurking images.

A body then . . . Start with that.

He remembered what bodies were. Arms, legs, head, torso . . . An intellectual vision of sex . . . Bodies, then . . .

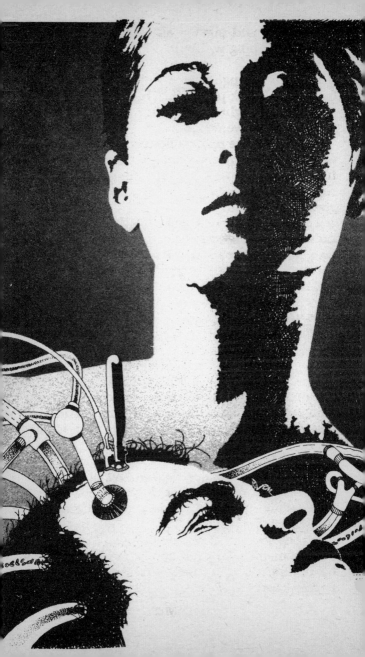

He thought of his arms, felt nothing. Tried to move them. There was no sense of their existence, let alone movement.

Breathing . . . He attempted to draw a deep breath. Nothing came into him. There was no indication of any boundary whatsoever between himself and the darkness and silence.

A buzzing tone began, directionless. It oscillated in volume. It rose in pitch, dropped to a rumble, returned to a buzz. Abruptly then, it shifted again, to word-like approximations he could not quite decipher.

There was a pause, as if for some adjustment. Then "Hello?" came clearly to him.

He felt a rush of relief mingled with fear. The word filled his mind, followed by immediate concern as to whether he had actually heard it.

"Hello?"

Again, then. The fear faded. Something close to joy replaced it. He felt an immediate need to respond.

"Yes? Hello? Who—"

His answer broke. How had he managed it? He felt the presence of no vocal mechanism. Yet he seemed to hear a faint echoing of his own reply, feedback-like, tinny. Where? Its source was not localized.

It seemed then that several voices were conversing—hurried, soft, distant. He could not follow the rush of their words.

Then, "Hello again. Please respond one time more. We are adjusting the speaker. How well do you hear us?"

"Clearly now," he answered. "Where am I? What has happened?"

"How much do you remember?"

"Nothing!"

"Panic not. Ernest Dawkins. Do you remember that your name is Ernest Dawkins? From your file, we have it."

"Now I do."

The simple statement of his name brought forth a series of images—his own face, his wife's, his two daughters', his apartment, the laboratory where he worked, his car, a sunny day at the beach . . .

That day at the beach . . . That was when he had first felt the pain in his left side—a dull ache at first, increasing over ensuing weeks. He had never been without it after that—until now, he suddenly realized.

"I—It's coming back—my memory," he said. "It's as if a dam had broken . . . Give me a minute."

"Take your time."

He shied away from the thought of the pain. He had been ill, very ill, hospitalized, operated upon, drugged . . . He—

He thought instead of his life, his family, his work. He thought of school and love and politics and research. He thought of the growing world tensions, and of his childhood, and—

"Are you right all, Ernest Dawkins?"

He had lost track of time, but that question caused him to produce something like a laugh, from somewhere.

"Hard to tell," he said. "I've been remembering—things. But as to whether I'm all right— Where the hell am I? What's happened?"

"Then you have remembered not everything?"

He noted odd inflections in the questioning voice, possibly even an accent that he could not place.

"I guess not."

"You were quite unwell."

"I remember that much."

"Dying, in fact. As they say."

He forced himself to return to the pain, to look beyond it.

"Yes," he acknowledged. "I remember."

. . . And it was all there. He saw his last days in the hospital as his condition worsened, passing the point of no return, the faces of his family, friends and relatives wearing this realization. He recalled his decision to go through with an earlier resolution, long since set into motion. Money had never been a problem. It seemed it had always been there, in his family—his, by early inheritance—as ubiquitous as his attitude toward death after his parents' passing. Enough to have himself frozen for the long winter, to drop off dreaming of some distant spring . . .

"I recall my condition," he said. "I know what must finally have occurred."

"Yes," came the reply. "That is what happened."

"How much time has passed?"

"Considerable."

He would have licked his lips. He settled for the mental equivalent."

"My family?" he finally inquired.

"It has been too long."

"I see."

The other gave him time to consider this information. Then, "You had, of course, considered this possibility?"

"Yes. I prepared myself—as much as a man can—for such a state of affairs."

"It has been long. Very long . . ."

"How long?"

"Allow us to proceed in our own fashion, please."

"All right. You know your business best."

"We are glad that you are so reasonable a being."

"Being?"

"Person. Excuse we."

"I must ask something, though—not having to do with the passage of time: Is English now spoken as you speak it? Or is it not your native language?"

There was a sudden consultation, just beyond the range of distinguishability. There followed a high-pitched artifact. Then, "Also let us reserve that question," the reply finally came.

"As you would. Then will you tell me about my situation? I am more than a little concerned. I can't see or feel anything."

"We are aware of this. It is unfortunate, but there is no point in misrepresenting to you. The time has not yet come for your full arouse."

"I do not understand. Do you mean that there is no cure for my condition yet?"

"We mean that there is no means of thawing you without doing great damage."

"Then how is it that we are conversing?"

"We have lowered your temperature even more—near to the zero absolute. Your nervous system has become superconductor. We have laid induction field upon your brain and initiated small currents within. Third space, left side head and those movement areas for talk are now serving to activate mechanical speaker here beside we. We address you direct in the side of brain places for hearing talk."

There came another wave of panic. How long this one lasted, he did not know. Vaguely, he became aware of the voice again, repeating his name.

"Yes," he finally managed. "I understand. It is not

easy to accept . . ."

"We know. But this does you no damage," came the reply. "You might even take a heart from it, to know that you persist."

"There is that. I see your meaning and can take it as hope. But why? Surely you did not awaken me simply to demonstrate this?"

"No. We have interest in your times. Purely archaeologic."

"Archaeological! That would seem to indicate the passage of a great deal of time!"

"Forgive me. Perhaps we have chose wrong word, thinking of it in terms of ruins. But your nervous system is doorway to times past."

"Ruins! What the hell happened?"

"There was war, and there have been disasters. The record, therefore, is unclear."

"Who won the war?"

"That is difficult to say."

"Then it must have been pretty bad."

"We would assume this. We are still ourselves learning. That is why we seek to know time past from your cold remains."

"If there was all this chaos, how is it that I was preserved through it?"

"The cold-making units here are powered by atomic plant which ran well untended—save for computer—for long while, and entire establishment is underground."

"Really? Things must have changed quite a bit after my—enrollment —here. It wasn't set up that way at the time I read the prospectus and visited the place."

"We really know little of the history of this establishment. There are many things of which we are ignorant. That is why we want you to tell us about your times."

"It is difficult to know where to begin . . ."

"It may be better if we ask you questions."

"All right. But I would like answers to some of my own afterwards."

"A suitable arrangement. Tell us then: Did you reside at or near your place of employment?"

"No. Actually, I lived halfway across town and had to drive in every day."

"Was this common for the area and the country?"

"Pretty much so, yes. Some other people did use other means of transportation, of course. Some rode on buses. Some car-pooled. I drove. A lot of us did."

"When you say that you drove, are we to understand that you refer to four-wheeled land vehicle powered by internal combustion engine?"

"Yes, that is correct. They were in common use in the latter half of the twentieth century."

"And there were many such?"

"Very many."

"Had you ever problems involving presence of too many of them on trails at same time?"

"Yes. Certain times of day—when people were going to work and returning—were referred to as 'rush hour'. At such times there were often traffic jams—that is to say, so many vehicles that they got in one another's ways."

"Extremely interesting. Were such creatures as whales still extant?"

"Yes."

"Interesting, too. What sort of work did you do?"

"I was involved in research on toxic agents of a

chemical and bacteriological nature. Most of it was classified."

"What does that indicate?"

"Oh. It was of a secret nature, directed toward possible military application."

"Was war already in progress?"

"No. It was a matter of—preparedness. We worked with various agents that might be used, if the need ever arose."

"We think we see. Interesting times. Did you ever develop any of efficient nature?"

"Yes. A number of them."

"Then what would you do with them? It would seem hazardous to have such materials about during peace."

"Oh, samples were stored with the utmost precaution in very safe places. There were three main caches, and they were well-sheltered and well-guarded."

There was a pause. Then, "We find this somewhat distressing," the voice resumed. "Do you feel they might have survived—a few, some centuries?"

"It is possible."

"Being peace-loving, we are naturally concerned with items dangerous to human species—"

"You make it sound as if you are not yourself a member."

There came another high-pitched artifact. Then, "The language has changed more even than we realized. Apologies. Wrong inference taken. Our desire, to deactivate these dangerous materials. Long have we expected their existences. You perhaps will advise? Their whereabouts unknown to us."

"I'm—not—so sure—about that," he answered.

"No offense meant, but you are only a voice to me. I really know nothing about you. I'm not certain that I should give this information."

There was a long silence.

"Hello? Are you still there?" he tried to say.

He heard nothing, not even his own voice. Time seemed to do strange things around him. Had it stopped for a moment? Had he given offense? Had this questioner dropped dead?

"Hello! Hello!" he said. "Do you hear me?"

". . . Mechanical failure," came the reply. "Apologies for. Sorry about yesterday."

"Yesterday!"

"Turned you off while obtaining new speaker. Just when you were to say where best poisons are."

"I am sorry," he stated. "You have asked for something that I cannot, in good conscience, give to you."

"We wish only to prevent damage."

"I am in the terrible position of having no way to verify anything that is told me."

"If something heavy falls upon you, you break like bottle."

"I could not even verify whether that had occurred."

"We could turn you off again, turn off the cold-maker."

"At least it would be painless," he said with more stoicism than he felt.

"We require this information."

"Then you must seek it elsewhere."

"We will disconnect your speaker and your hearer and go away. We will leave you thinking in the middle of nothing. Good-bye now."

"Wait!"

"Then you will tell us?"

"No. I—can't . . ."

"You will go mad if we disconnect these things, will you not?"

"I suppose so. Eventually . . ."

"Must we do it, then?"

"Your threats have shown me what you are like. I cannot give you such weapons."

"Ernest Dawkins, you are not intelligent being."

"And you are not an archaeologist. Or you would do future generations the service of turning me off, to save the other things that I do know."

"You are right. We are not such. You will never know what we are."

"I know enough."

"Go to your madness."

Silence again.

For a long while the panic held him. Until the images of his family recurred, and his home, and his town. These grew more and more substantial, and gradually he came to walk with them and among them. Then, after a time, he stopped reporting for work and spent his days at the beach. He wondered at first when his side would begin to hurt. Then he wondered why he had wondered this. Later, he forgot many things, but not the long days beneath the sun or the sound of the surf, the red rain, the blue, or the melting statue with the fiery eyes and the sword in its fist. When he heard voices under the sand he did not answer. He listened instead to whales singing to mermaids on migrating rocks, where they combed their long green hair with shards of bone, laughing at the lightning and the ice. ●

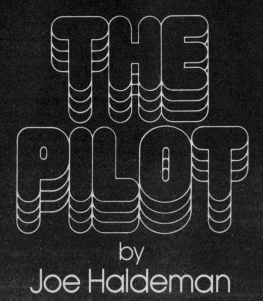

THE PILOT

by
Joe Haldeman

To fall ever Outward: a fate worse than death? Oh, ecstasy of flight!

The set is out of adjustment: a green streak slashes diagonally through the viewing cube, impales the smiling host.

She tries to adjust it by softly licking a molar, remembers, curses economically, turns a knob until the streak disappears, another knob to sharpen the image. Host smiling goodbye to someone. Feel of cold metal sticks to her thumb and finger until she rubs it away on her thigh, disgusted, nose wrinkling. How many filthy traveling salesmen and conventioneers and hotel maids have touched these knobs since they were last sterilized? Have they ever been sterilized?

"Our next guest is a woman with a marvelously rare occupation." *Occupation*! He smiles offcube and the picture scale diminishes to include her as well, not smiling, trying not to fidget on the filthy leather chair. "She is a spaceship pilot . . ." *I am a spaceship.* ". . . but no ordinary rocket jock. She pilots a slowboat between the Earth and the outer solar system—the asteroids, even as far as Saturn. Her name is Lydia Meinenger and she's a fellow New Yorker." *New Yorker*. "Lydia, would you tell us something about slowboats; how they—"

"In the first place," she interrupts, "they aren't slow. They go much faster than anything you use in the Earth-Moon system. The name is a hangover from the old robot tugs that crawled along on Hohmann transfer orbits, to minimize fuel use. A Hohmann tug took six years to get to Saturn; I can make it in thirteen months. Nine months, with a Jupiter flyby. But I can't do that with passengers."

"Because of the radiation?"

"That's right." *Warm like summer sunshine.* "They can't wrap everyone up in lead, the way I am."

"That's probably the most fascinating aspect of your job, Lydia. The way you're wired up to the ship, you're actually part of it." *I am the ship, you actual fool.*

" 'Wired up' is a little extreme. They don't use surgical implants any more, but just induction plates pasted over various organs. There are a few small wires associated with the somatic feedback system," *O slow ecstasy*, "but they enter through natural body openings and you hardly feel them once they're in place."

"This feedback thing, this is how you control the ship?"

"That's right. There's an initial calibration that, well, as long as I feel good," *Good!* "then every system in the ship is working properly. If any system varies from its expected performance, I feel it as an illness or slight pain. The nature and intensity of the wrongness tells me which system is involved and gives me an idea as to the severity of the malfunction. For instance, a hydrogen ullage problem, where the fuel flow is momentarily uneven, I feel as a hot spasm of—"Screen goes white, low chime, "—tum."

Host smirking behind filthy hand. "Afraid the censor won't let *that* slip by, Lydia." *They live in shit so can't talk about it?* Chuckles. "It doesn't seem very precise."

"The important thing is sensitivity, not precision. Instantly knowing which system is hurting. Then I can call up the appropriate system parameters and compare them to the ideal mission profile. I can usually fix the trouble with the help of the ship's diagnostic library. If not, I call Company Control on the Moon."

"So your main job is troubleshooting."

"Yes." *Like you troubleshoot your body? Filthy fool couldn't find your liver with both hands.* "I make decisions regarding the maintenance of the ship."

"It doesn't sound very exciting . . ."

"It is."

Looking at her expectantly; she doesn't continue. "You must have quite a technical background." *For a woman, say it fool.*

"No. I majored in classical Latin and Greek. The technical part is easy. Any reasonably intelligent woman could do it."

"I, uh, see . . . you—"

"There are no male slowboat pilots. I don't suppose your censor wants me to discuss that. You'll just have to go ask a twelve-year-old." She flashes him a bright metal smile. "Much nicer than—" Chime.

Weak try at an urbane chuckle. "There's an in-

teresting side benefit to your job. I'll bet viewers would be surprised to know how old you are."

'She lets him wait just long enough; as he opens his mouth to save himself: "Sixty-five."

"Now, isn't that marvelous? You could pass for twenty."

"As could anybody who didn't have to contend with gravity and sun and wind and this—" Chime. "—that passes for your food and drink and air. I've spent most of my life immersed in oxygenated fluorocarbon, weightless, fed a perfect diet, exercised by machines."

"But your job is dangerous."

"Not very. Perhaps one in thirty is lost."

"More dangerous than holovision." His image turns a little fuzzy; she touches the filthy knob to sharpen him. "The atomic drive itself must be hazardous." Carries her contaminated hand into the bathroom, listening. "Not to mention meteors and—" *Fool.*

"No, actual catastrophes are very rare." She washes the offended fingers carefully. "The dangerous time is turnaround, when the ship is going with maximum velocity. It's supposed to flip and slow down for the last half of the journey." Leaves the soap on warm clean fingers. "Sometimes they don't flip, though; just keep going, faster and faster. Too fast for the Company's rescue ship."

"How terrible." Standing in front of the set, dry hand tugs elastic, urgent. *Clothes!* "They just keep going . . ."

"Forever." *Ecstasy, O!* "The pilot may live for centuries."

"Well . . . if ever a cliche was true . . . that does sound like a fate worse than death." *Fool.*

She nods soberly. "Indeed it does." *Fool, fool, O damn, doesn't last this way.* She sinks back onto the bed and starts to cry. *Fry them dead.*

He puts a filthy finger to his lips. "Well. Are you, um, going to be on Earth long?"

"Only another two days." Hurting herself, she stops, wipes eyes, soap sting brings new tears. "I like being back in New York, but the gravity is tiring. The air makes me cough. I look forward to going out again." *Last time, fry the bastards.*

"Saturn this time?"

"No, for a change I'm going to the inner system. Taking 500 colonists to the new Venus settlement." *Taking them to burn.*

"Is that more dangerous? I mean, I don't know much about space, but isn't there a danger that you could fall into the Sun?"

She smiles politely. "No, none." Sharp metal

teeth, she runs her tongue along behind her teeth but the switches aren't connected. "It would take as much energy to 'fall' into the Sun as it takes to escape from the Solar System." *Less to skim it, though, fry.* "All that gravity. I suppose it might be possible; I've never made the calculation." *Characteristic velocity 17.038 emos, exit inclination 0.117 rad, goodbye solar system, goodbye filth.*

Blank stare. "Yes . . . oh, Jimmy's giving me the signal." *Right at perihelion, goose it all the way up, emergency override, nineteen gees, crush their dry baked bodies into dust.* "I'm afraid we've run out of time."

Cargo shit baked to sterile dust. "We certainly have enjoyed having you here, Lydia." He holds out his hand and she looks at it.

Bound for the stars, forever young, the dear ship inside of my ecstasy. "Thank you."   ●

THE WAYS OF LOVE

by Poul Anderson

I could not love thee
half so much...

Ten of their years before, we had seen that being come through the transporter into our ship and die. This day we stood waiting upon his world, and as we waited, we remembered.

The *Fleetwing* was bound for Prime of that constellation for which she was named. She would not—will not—arrive there for many lifetimes, though already she had fared, at more than half the speed of light, while Arvel swung six hundred and twelve orbits around Sarnir. So deep is the universe. She was, indeed, the farthest out of all our ships, and Rero-and-I reckoned it an honor when we were assigned a term of service within her.

Not that we expected anything spectacular. Rather, it should be the opposite. Until the starcraft reach their goals, they are doing little but patiently traveling. A change of crew is almost like a casual rite. You and your mate go to the mattercasting station on Irjelan. The pair whom you are to relieve come back and inform you of conditions aboard. That seldom takes long and, as a rule, is done at ease, above a brazier of smokeleaf in the elders' lounge. (Yet you see Arvel shining green among the stars, over this scarred face of her outer moon, and feel what your duty will mean.) Soon you two give

he others a farewell twining of tendrils and make
our way to the appropriate sender unit. The flash
f energy which scans and disintegrates your
odies, atom by atom, you do not feel; it goes too
wiftly, as fast as the modulated tachyonic beam
vhich then leaps across the light-years. At the end,
he patterns which are you are rebuilt in new
atoms, and there you are for the next ninety-six
days.

You do maintenance, perhaps minor repair; you
record scientific observations and perhaps prog-
am new ones; you might start the engine for a
ourse correction, though rarely when the target
un is still remote, none of it takes much effort. Your
rue job is to stand by against improbable
emergencies. Sometimes a vessel in transit gets
ised as a relay station by a couple or a party bound
or too distant a world to make it in a single jump.
hen they stop for a short visit. This would happen
n *Fleetwing*, she being on our uttermost frontier
and bound onward into strangeness.

Rero-and-I welcomed the isolation. Our usual
vork was challenging. We had been pilot and chief
engineer on a series of exploratory boats in several
different planetary systems, which meant assisting
he teams after landing them. Perforce, we became
a pair of jackleg xenologists. This in turn involved
us in the proceedings of the Stellar Institute back
on Arvel, its rather hectic social rounds as well as its
data evaluations. We couldn't plead family needs
when we would have preferred to stay home, since
both our children were young adults. Nor did we
want more; an infant would ground us. We enjoyed
too much what we did in space. Its price was that
we had too little life for ourselves.

Thus we were glad of aloneness wherein to meditate, read, watch classic choreodramas on tape, really get to know certain music and fragrances, be altogether at leisure in our lovemaking. And so it went for seven and thirty days

Then the alarm whistled, the warning panels flashed, we hastened to the receiving chamber. As we floated waiting in free fall, I sensed how both my hearts knocked. Rero's body and mine worked to cool us down from the heat of our excitement; we hung in a mist and our odors were heady, we gripped hands and wished we could join flesh. What cause had anyone to seek us out? A messenger, telling of catastrophe?

He materialized, and we knew the disaster was not ours but his.

Our first shock at his appearance blent with the pain that sent us hurtling back, a-gasp. A puff of the atmosphere in his ship had come through with him. I recognized the lethal acridity of oxygen. Fortunately, there was not more than our air renewers could clean out in a hurry. Meanwhile he died, in agony, trying to breathe chlorine.

We returned to attend his drifting corpse. Silence poured in from the unseen dark, through the barren metal around us, as if to drown our spirits. We looked long upon him — not then aware that he was male, for the human genitals are as peculiar as the human psyche. His odors were salt and sour, few and simple. We wondered if that was because he was dead. (It wasn't, of course.) After we had carefully, reverently opened his soiled coverall and inner garments, we spent a while trying to see what kind of beauty might be his. He looked grotesquely like us and unlike us: also a biped, larger than Rero, smaller than me, with five digits to a hand, no part truly resembling anything of ours. Most striking, perhaps, was the skin. Save for patches of hair and a scattering of it everywhere else, that skin was smooth, yellowish-white, devoid of color-change cells and vapor vents. I wondered how such a folk expressed themselves, their deepest feelings, to each other. (I still do.) Eeriest to me, somehow, were the eyes. He had two, the same as us, but in that tendrilless, weirdly convoluted visage their blindness glimmered white around blue . . . blue.

Rero whispered at last: "Another intelligent race. The first we've met that explores too. The very first. And this one of them had to come through to our ship unprotected, and die. How could it happen?"

I sent look and fingers along the body, as gently as might be. His aura was fading away fast. Oh, yes, I know it's only infrared radiation; I am not an Incar-

nationist. Nevertheless, that dimming after death is like a sign of the final wayfaring. "Emaciation may be normal to the species, and the society may be careless about cleanliness," I said in my driest tone. "I doubt both, though, and suspect that here has been a terrible accident consequent upon an earlier misfortune." Meanwhile I thought the old goodbye: *God take home your soul, God shelter it in the warmth of His pouch and nourish it with the milk of Her udder, until that which was you has grown and may go free.*

Rero joined me in speculations which proved to be essentially correct. Since the truth has never become as widely known on Arvel as it should be, let me set it briefly forth.

The *Southern Cross* was likewise among the oldest and farthest-out vessels from her world. She likewise was bound for the brightest star in the constellation for which she was named, the same as we desired; humans call that sun Alpha Crucis. Like us, they use mattercasters to alternate the watches in space. This craft had chanced to pass near enough a burnt-out black dwarf that they changed her program and put her in orbit around it for scientific study. Four males went to initiate this. Unforeseen factors, chiefly the enormous magnetic field of the object, wrecked both their ion drive and their transmitter. Two of them died in the effort to make repairs. The two survivors were starving when at last they had put together a primitive 'caster. Not knowing its constants with exactness, they must vary the tuning until they got the signal of a receiving station. When they did, David Ryerson rushed impulsively through. It chanced that he had not tuned to a human-built circuit, but to ours aboard *Fleetwing*.

Soon I warned Rero: "We must respond, and fast, before whoever is at the other end switches to a different code and we lose contact."

"Yes," she agreed. Her aura flamed with eagerness, though at the same time her touch honored the dead. "By the dawn, what a miracle! A whole race as advanced as us, but surely knowing things we don't—a whole transporter network linked to ours—O unknown friend, rejoice in your fate!"

"I'll armor myself and take the reamins along," I said. "That ought to demonstrate good will."

"What?" Her smells, vapor cloud, color-change cells gone black, showed horror. She clutched my arm till claws dug in. "Alone? Voah, no!"

I drew her to me. "It will be a gray fire to depart from you, Rero, my life, not knowing if . . . if I condemn you to widowhood thereby. Yet one of us must, and one must stay behind, to tend the ship and bear the news home if the other cannot. I think female agility won't count for much, when yonder hull isn't likely to be bigger than this, and male strength may count for a little."

She did not resist long, for in fact her common sense exceeds mine. It was only that *I* had to say the word first. We did not even stop to make love. But never have I seen a red more pure than was in her glance upon me when we embraced.

And so I, protected against poison, entered the transmitter and emerged on the *Southern Cross* with David Ryerson's body in my arms. His shipmate, Terangi Maclaren, received it in awe. Afterward, Rero-and-I helped him find the tuning for a station maintained by his race, and he trod across the gulf between, bearing death and glory.

—There followed the dozen years—ten of Earth's—that everyone knows about, when commissions from the two species met in neutral spots; when a few representatives sent to either planet brought home bewilderment; when meanwhile the scientists jointly hammered out sufficient knowledge that they could guess how vast was their ignorance. My wife and I were concerned in this effort, not merely because first contact had chanced to be ours, but because our prior experience with sophonts had given us a leap ahead. To be sure, those were all primitives, whereas now Arvel was dealing with a civilization that sundered the atom, rebuilt the gene, and colonized across interstellar distances. Here too, however, we were well equipped. she to seek converse with fellow pilots, I with fellow engineers.

Accordingly, when the Earthfolk, to whom ten is

a special number, decided to celebrate the decade with ceremonies, and invited Arvelan participation, it was natural that Rero-and-I go. Apart from symbolism, we might be of practical use. Thus far the two breeds had shared hardly anything except those technical endeavors. The time was overpast for agreements. Most obviously, though not exclusively: If we could combine our mattercaster webs, then we would each have access to about twice as much space as before, twice the wealth, twice as many homesites—

No, not really. In that respect, Arvel would gain less, inasmuch as the Sarnirian System has a cosmically unusual distribution of elements. Planets where photosynthesis liberates chlorine are more rare than those where it liberates oxygen, not to mention additional requirements. (My brother mariner, David Ryerson, with calcium instead of silicon in his bones. . . .) Many people in our families and tribes felt ungenerous about this, wanted compensation for the difference. Meanwhile on Earth—well, that is what I wish to relate, if I am able. Certainly both sides were haunted: *How far can we trust them? They command energies which can break a world apart.*

Ostensibly present for harmless rituals, Rero-and-I meant to talk privately, informally with powerful humans, helping lay the groundwork for a conference that could arrive at a treaty. That was our plan, when eagerly we agreed to go.

It made our disappointment the fierier, after we had been on Earth for a time. And in this wise happened that we stood on a terrace waiting to be borne to a secret rendezvous.

Once a fortress in a frightful age, later remodeled

and enlarged to hold the masters of the globe, that complex called the Citadel dwells magnificently among those mountains called the Alps. From the parapet we looked down steeps and cliffs which tumbled into a valley. Beyond it the heights lifted anew, a waterfall ashine like a drawn blade, a blue-shadowed whiteness blanketing peaks, the greenish gleam of a solid mass. This is a chill planet where water often freezes, a sight which can be lovely. The sun stood close to midday in a wan heaven, its disc seeming slightly larger than that of Sarnir above Arvel but its light muted. Not only does it give off less ultraviolet, the air absorbs most of what there is. Yet Rero-and-I had learned to see beauty in soft golden-hued luminance, in a thousand shy tints across eldritch landscapes.

"I wish—"Wind boomed hollowly around Rero's voice. She broke off, for she had no real need to

speak her thought. Through the transparent seal-suit, face-tendrils and skin-language said for her how she would joy to inhale, smell, drink, taste, feel, take the wholeness of this place unto herself. Impossible, of course, unless she first hooked into a pain inhibitor; and then she would have a bare moment for the orgasm of body comprehension, before the oxygen killed her. Poor David Ryerson, had he known what awaited him he might at least have died observing, not bewildered.

I took her by the hand, glove in glove. My own desire was as strong as hers, but directed toward her. She saw that, and saucily flexed her sex organ at me . . . but the rest of her declared longing rather than humor. Imagine for yourself and your mate: the entire time you spend outside an Arvel-conditioned suite, which is most of the time, you are enveloped apart from each other!

"Do you think Tamara Ryerson will be present?" I asked, more for the talk than out of curiosity.

"Who?—Ai, yes, David Ryerson's widow," Rero said. We had met her just once, at a welcoming ceremony which included Terangi Maclaren. This was at the beginning of our visit, and no opportunity came to converse with either of them. An omen—for when had we since gotten to link minds in fullness and candor with anybody? "I'd hardly expect that." My wife paused. "Although, now you mention it, we might well try to seek her out later. What does widowhood mean to her? That could give us a clue to the whole psychology of these beings."

"I doubt that, from a single sample" I answered. "However . . . n-n-n-n . . . one sample is better than none. Maybe Vincent Indigo can arrange it." A short, brightly-clad human came out of a doorway. "Name the Illwisher and you'll sense his heat."

My use of the proverb was figurative. Our Citadel-appointed guide, liaison, arranger, and general factotum had been tirelessly helpful. True, we soon got a feeling of being rushed from spot to spot, person to person, event to event, with never an instant free for getting acquainted. But when we complained of this to him—

"Good day, Sir Voah, Lady Rero," he said with a salute. "I'm sorry I'm late. If we're to get you away from here unbeknownst, you can't be seen leaving. A Guards officer was inspecting the area and I had to wait till he finished."

Our throatstrings could not form his kind of sounds very clearly, but a minicomputer passed our words through a transponder which corrected that. I admired the device. In spite of more experience with aliens, we Arvelans had never developed anything as good for this purpose. On their side, human members of the study group had expressed immense interest in some of our construction technology. What might our peoples not accomplish together, if they would allow themselves? "It is in order, then, on the island of Taiwan?" I asked.

Vincent Indigo nodded. "Yes, the Maclarens are ready for you. It'll be dark there and the house has big, well-shaped grounds. We can set you down and take off again afterward without being noticed. Come on, we'd better not dawdle here."

As we strode over the flagstones, I could not help fretting. This world was so full of mysteries, riddles less of nature than of the soul. "How long can we stay? You weren't certain about that."

"No, because it depended on what arrangements I could make. The idea is to get you together with him for completely free conversation—no officials around, no busybodies, no journalists. And it has to stay secret that you did, or the whole project is spoiled from the start, right? Knowing you'd be questioned about it afterward would inhibit things, no matter how well-meant the questions. Voah, my friend, you can't escape being a first-magnitude celebrity."

If you want to feel our problem, consider those few sentences. I can hardly translate the key words; you notice what archaic and foreign terms I am borrowing, in search of rough equivalents.

Officials: Not parents, not tribal elders, not Speakers for an Alliance or their executive servants—no, agents of that huge bloodless organization called a "government," which claims the right to slay whomever resists the will of its dominators. *Busybodies:* Without sanction of kinship, custom, or dire need, certain humans will still thrust themselves into affairs. *Journalists:* Professional collectors and disseminators of news recognize no bounds upon their activities except for what is imposed by the government; and is that limitation not odd in itself? *Celebrity:* Lest the foregoing make Earthfolk seem repulsive, let me say that they have a wonderful capacity for giving admiration, respect, yes, a kind of love to persons they have never met individually and to whom they have no kinship whatsoever.

I pass over the fact that Indigo addressed me alone, ignoring Rero. That might be a simple peculiarity of language, when it was I who had spoken to him.

"Twenty-four hours looks reasonable," he told me—a rotation period of the planet, slightly longer than Arvel's. "The Protector is making an important speech tomorrow, you see, which'll draw everybody's attention away from you."

"Indeed?" said Rero. "Should we not join in heeding your . . . your head of state?"

"If you want." Indigo gave a very Arvelan-like shrug. "However, I'm told it'll be on internal matters—currency stabilization, ethnic discontents, revolutionary sentiment on certain colonial worlds and how we should quell it—nothing which makes any difference to you, I should think."

"I don't know what *I* should think," she blurted, and gave up. What we had heard hovered on the edge of making sense but was never quite seizable, like a chant in a dream. Could we ever win enough

understanding of these creatures that we would dare trust them?

Indigo led us down a staircase hewn from the rock, to a lower level where a hangar stood open. Despite lessened weight here, I was glad to see that end of our walk. The water-circulation unit felt heavy on my back. Humans who come to Arvel have an advantage over us in that regard, needing less life support apparatus. Their survival depends more on maintaining a particular range of temperatures than it does on maintaining a temperature differential.

We climbed into the spearhead craft which waited for us and reclined into specially modified seats. An attendant connected our suits to a pair of full-cycle biostatic units in the rear of the cabin, greatly increasing our comfort. "Relax, friends," Indigo urged. "This is a suborbital jet, you remember.

We'll reach Taiwan in an hour."

"You are kind to us," Rero said. Calm and cool, her gratitude laved me as well.

The human's beaky countenance crinkled in what he could have called a smile. It is a large part of their meager body language. "No, no, milady," he replied. "I get paid for assisting you."

"But is this not . . . unauthorized, is that the word? Don't you risk trouble for yourself, if your elders accuse you afterward of having acted unwisely?"

The bars of hair above his eyes drew together. "Only if something goes wrong and they find out. I admit it could happen, though it's very unlikely. As I've tried to explain to you, we have antisocial elements on Earth, criminals, political or religious fanatics, lunatics. They could make you a target. That's why the Citadel's had you closely guarded and kept you to a strict itinerary. But since this is a secret trip, we ought to be safe, and I do want to oblige you whenever possible."

The aircraft rolled forth and lifted easily, as if on a quite ordinary flight. Not until we were in the stratosphere did she unleash her entire strength. Then stars blinked into view, the planet became a many-marbled immensity, we soared above a continent which dwarfed any upon Arvel until we began slanting down again toward the ocean east of it. Silence prevailed among the passengers. Indigo puffed nervously on a series of smokesticks, the cabin attendants watched a television show, the crew were elsewhere. I knew no reason to be taut, but my hearts thudded ever more loud and I saw that Rero felt the same. To the minute degree that sight and touch, nothing more, permitted, we spent most of the journey making love.

Night was young over the island, Earth's single moon rising full. The Maclaren home stood by itself, likewise on a mountain though one that held trees and gardens to the top. Our craft descended silently, as a glider, probably unnoticed save by a traffic control computer or two. For lack of a proper landing strip such as its size required, it employed a straight stretch of road which bore no traffic at this hour. I admired the pilot's skill. More did I admire Indigo's, in gathering information and making arrangements. To do that when the Protector's spies seemed to be everywhere struck me as remarkable.

The flyer halted by an upward-bending side road. Our man peered through a window. "He's here, waiting," he said. "Go on out. Fast, before somebody else happens by. We've got to scramble. I'll be back for you at this time tomorrow evening."

We had already been unplugged from the biostats and had restarted our portable units. They could maintain us that long, though not much more. Food would be dried rations shoved through a helmet lock, drink would be water sucked from a tube, waste release would be into an aspirator, rest would be uneasy and sexual intercourse nil. However, if we could achieve real converse, it would be worth everything. We scrambled forth with eagerness making our auras dance. The flyer taxied off at once, rounded a curve, and vanished. After a moment we heard a rumble and saw it take off above the shoulder of the mountain, an upward meteor.

Terangi Maclaren stood shadowlike in the dim light, save for his own deep-colored radiation. "Welcome," he said, and briefly clasped our gloves.

We'll have to walk; those rigs of yours wouldn't fit in my car. Follow me, please." I decided he was this curt because he likewise was anxious to get us hidden.

Trees turned the drive into a gut of darkness. We switched on our flashlights. "Can you do without those? Maclaren asked. "That blue-white isn't like anything a local person would use."

Rero-and-I doused them. "Suppose we link hands and you lead us," she suggested. When we had done this, she wondered, "Are you indeed worried about the possibility of our being observed? Can you not deny curiosity seekers access to your—" She groped for a word. They do not seem to have kin-right on Earth. "Your property?"

"Yes, but gossip might reach the wrong ears," he explained. "That could bring on trouble."

"Of what kind? Surely you do nothing . . . unlawful? . . . in receiving us."

"Technically no." By now I believed I had learned the nuances of the human voice sufficiently well to hear bitterness in his. "But the Citadel has ways to make things unpleasant. For instance, you may recall I'm an astrophysicist. These days I'm directing a survey in detail of the stars we have access to—expensive. By hinting that funds might otherwise be cut off, a bureaucrat could get me dismissed. And I do have independent means, but I'm a little old to go back to playboying."

Footfalls resounded loud on the pavement, through a rustle of leaves in a sea breeze. I toiled up the mountainside under a burden of gear, in a cramped loneliness of my own scents and no other. The night of Earth pressed inward.

"Of course," Maclaren went on after a while, "I

may be borrowing grief. It's no secret that I'm strongly in favor of close relationships with Arvel. To date, that hasn't caused many obstacles to get thrown in my way—though it hasn't been exactly smoothed for me either. My talking to you in private needn't necessarily alarm the Protector and his loyalists. It might even encourage people in the government who agree with me. I just can't tell. Therefore, let's be as cautious as practical.

"Besides," he added, "there are individuals, yes, organizations that hate the idea of making alliance with you. They could do something rash, if they knew you were here unguarded."

Indigo had intimated the same. Rero-and-I had failed to understand. "*Why?*" I asked into the darkness. "Yes, I realize many will be wary of us because we are an unknown quantity. We have their kind on Arvel. In fact, frankly, sir, the pair of us came largely in hopes of learning more about your kind."

"A hope that has been frustrated," Rero put in. "We have become convinced we are deliberately being hurried along and kept busy, in order that we will return home still ignorant . . . or downright suspicious."

"Terangi Maclaren," I said, "you speak as if more is involved than exaggerated prudence. You give the impression that certain humans want to isolate humanity from us on principle."

"That is the impression I meant to give," he replied.

Through my glove I felt how his clasp tightened. I returned the tension to him, and Rero shared it with me.

"I'm not sure how clear I can make the situation," Maclaren said with care. "Your institutions are so utterly unlike ours—your beliefs, your ways of looking at the universe and living in it, everything—Well, that's part of the problem. For instance, the Hiroyama Report. Do you know about that? Hiroyama tried to find out what your major religions are. Her book created a sensation. If a powerful, scientifically oriented culture can hold that God is love . . . with sex apparently the major part of love—well, that defies a lot of old-established Terrestrial orthodoxies. Heresies spring up, which provokes reaction. Oh, yes, Hiroyama did mention that Arvelans practice monogamy and fidelity, or so she thought. She couldn't be sure, because their spokesmen never described this as a moral requirement. Therefore the new human cults, most of them, go in for orgies and promiscuity."

Though we had encountered curious sexual patterns elsewhere, Rero still faltered in surprise: "Mating for life—what else can we do?"

"Never mind now," Maclaren said bleakly. "It's a single example of why some groups on Earth would like to ring down the curtain forever on contact with Arvel. And by extension, with any other high-level civilization we may come upon. For practical purposes, what matters is why the Protector fears alliance, and his followers do.

"You see, the Citadel already has a nearly impossible job, trying to keep control over the human race, including settlers on the colonial planets and the societies they're developing. Disaffection, subversion, repeated attempts at rebellion—You mean you Arvelans have never had similar woes?"

"Why should we?" I asked in my bemusement.

Did the vague ruddiness of his aura show him nodding? "I'm not too surprised, Voah-and-Rero."

(He was that familiar with our mores. Hope blossomed small within me.) "Since you don't have anything we could call a proper government, you avoid its troubles and costs. To be sure, we're a different breed; what works for you probably wouldn't for us. Just the same, already quite a few thinkers are wondering aloud and in print if we really need a state sitting on us as heavily as the Citadel does. Given close, ongoing relationships with you, the next generation may well decide we don't need the Citadel at all.

"Besides that, well, simply doubling the space available to us, the number of planets we can occupy, that alone will soon make us ungovernable as a whole. We'll explode in a million different directions, and God Himself can only guess at the ultimate consequences. But a single thing is certain. It will bring down the Protectorate.

"Oh, our present lord can doubtless live out his reign. His son after him . . . maybe, maybe not. His grandson: impossible. And he isn't stupid. He knows it.

"At the same time, the Dynasty does still command powerful loyalties. A lot of people fear change for its own sake — not altogether unreasonably. They have a big stake in the existing order of things, and would like to pass it on to their children.

"Others — well, for them it's more emotional, down in the marrow, therefore more strong and dangerous. I don't know if you can imagine, Rero-and-Voah, what grip the Dynasty has on a man whose fathers served it these past three hundred years. What are *your* mystiques?"

We didn't try to answer that. The thought gave

me a faint shock: that I too probably lived by commitments so deep-seated that I didn't know they could override my reason. I heard Rero say, "You yourself would open the portal wide between our races, would you not, Terangi Maclaren? And surely many are with you."

"Right," he told us. "In and out of the government, there's a mighty sentiment in favor of going ahead. We feel stifled, and we want to let in a clean wind we can hear blowing. . . . Yes, it's a delicate balance of forces, or a multi-sided political struggle, or whatever metaphor you prefer. I do believe Arvelans and Earthlings are overdue for getting some real depth-psychological empathy with each other. That ought to clear away suspicion, ought to give the movement for freedom overwhelming strength." His tones, hitherto low, lifted. "How glad I am you came here."

The drive debouched on a level stretch of ground, the woods yielded to openness, and we were again out in light. To Maclaren, with his superior night vision, the view must have been magnificent, for even I found it beautiful. On our right the mountain rose further, on our left it plunged downward, in frosted shadowiness where here and there gleamed yellow the windows of a home. Far off on the seashore, a village twinkled in countless colors. Beyond reached the ocean, like living obsidian bridged by moonglade. Across the sky glimmered the galaxy. Everywhere else were individual stars, each of them a sun.

Maclaren led us among flowerbeds and across a wide stretch of lawn, to his house. It was low and rambling, the roof curved high; it had been built largely of timber, according to a pattern that I felt must be ancient in these parts; I wished very much that I could savor it with unmuffled senses. A lantern lighted a verandah. As we mounted this, the main door opened. A female human stood in the glow that poured out from behind her.

We knew her at once. Not being sure we would, Maclaren said, "Do you remember my wife, from the program we were on together when you arrived? Tamara." In the flicker of bright and black across Rero's skin, I saw my own shock mirrored. New as we then were to Earth, we had not caught any mention of Tamara's closeness to Maclaren. His wife? But she was David Ryerson's widow.!

We were inside the house before I was enough past my agitation to see that Maclaren had noticed it. Perhaps Tamara had too. Her manner was most gentle as she bowed her head above her hands laid together and murmured, "Be welcome, honored guests. It grieves us that we cannot offer refreshment. Is there any way we can minister to your needs or comfort?"

I saw that seats were provided to fit us in our sealsuits. Otherwise the room was long and lovely. Strange environment does not change the laws of harmonious proportion; swirls of wood grain in the floor, hues and textures of vegetable mats, were foreign but serene; a crystal bowl on a table held a stone and a flower, beneath a scroll of calligraphy that we did not have to read in order to admire; bookshelves breathed forth a promise; windows gave outlook on the night land, the sea, and the cosmos. A music player lilted notes of a piece that Rero-and-I had long ago told human members of the commission we enjoyed; the form is called *raga*. An incense stick burned, but of course I could only smell the manifold acridities of my own confined flesh.

"You are kind," Rero said. "Still, are you not being overly formal? Voah-and-I came in hopes of . . . of close understanding."

"Then why don't you sit?" Maclaren invited. He and Tamara waited till we had. She perched forward in her chair, fingers twined on her lap. In a long skirt and brief blouse, her skin was golden-brown, her form abstractly pleasing to us. Framed by flowing blue-black hair, her eyes were like the bright darkness outside. Maclaren was tall for an Earthling, he stood with half his torso raised above Rero while his head reached well up on my chest. Seated, he assumed an attitude as casual as his tubular garments, lounged back with ankle over knee—but his gaze never left us and I recognized gravity on his face.

"What had you in mind, Rero-and-Voah?" he began.

We were silent a while, until I trilled a laugh of sorts and admitted, "We are seeking what questions to ask, and how."

Tamara confirmed my guess about her perception when she inquired, "What surprised you on the verandah?"

Again we must hesitate. Finally Rero said, "We do not wish to give offense."

Maclaren waved a hand. "Let that be taken for granted on both sides, hm?" he suggested. "We might well drop something ourselves that you don't like. In that case, tell us, and we'll all try to find out why, and maybe we can get a little enlightenment from it."

"Well, then—" Regardless, Rero must summon her courage. "Tamara Ryerson, is that your proper name now? You are wedded to Terangi Maclaren?"

"Why, yes, for the past eight years," the human female replied. "Didn't you know?"

I tried to explain that the information had gone by us because of its alienness. Astonished in her turn, she exclaimed, "Doesn't it seem natural to you? Terangi and David were friends, shipmates. When Terangi came back, he found me alone with my baby, and helped me—at first for David's sake, but soon—Would you consider it wrong?"

"No," I said hastily. "We Arvelans also differ in our customs and beliefs, from culture to culture."

"Although," Rero added, "none of our kind would remarry . . . that quickly, I think. A young person who was widowed might remarry, but after several years."

"An older one?" Tamara asked softly.

"As a rule, they go asexual—celibate, if I remember your word aright," I told her. Fearing she might regard that as cruel: "This has been an honorable estate in every country and era. In civilized milieus, institutions have existed, such as . . . lodges, would you call them? . . . to give the widowed a solid place, a new belonginess."

"Why can't they remarry, though?"

"Few societies have actually forbidden remarriage at any age. It's just that few persons want to, who've had a mate for a long while."

Maclaren made a chuckling noise. "And yet, as far as I can tell," he remarked, "you Arvelans are hornier than us humans, which is saying a lot."

I exchanged a look, a handclasp, and a sexual signal with Rero.

"What makes the difference?" Tamara wondered. "Sorrow?"

"No, sorrow wears away, if I use that word correctly," I answered, doubtful whether I did. (Afterward that doubt was to grow. Do they indeed mourn as we do?) "But think, please. Precisely because of the close relationship, personalities have blended. Remarriage involves changing one's entire spirit, that originally developed in young adulthood after the first wedding. Not many individuals want to become somebody quite different. Of those who might wish to, not many dare attempt it."

Sensing Tamara's puzzlement, Rero said in her most scientific manner:

"It has long been obvious that sexual dimorphism is greater among Arvelans than among Earthlings. In your species, the female both carries the child to term and nurses it afterward. Among us, she carried the fetus a much shorter time, then delivers it and gives it to the male, who puts it in his pouch. There it has shelter and temperature differentials till it has matured enough to venture forth. However, the mother does provide nourishment for the infant from special glands—milk, is that your word? This means the male must always be close to her, to hand the infant over for feeding. It means, too, that he must be large and strong. That leaves her free, in an evolutionary sense, to become small but agile. Our presapient ancestors hunted in male-female teams, as savages did within historical times. Civilizations have not changed that basic partnership; most work has always been organized so as to be done by mated couples. The interdependence goes beyond the physical, into the psyche. Among the primitive peoples, the widowed have generally pined away. A large part of our history and sociology has turned on the provision of various means to give the asexual a survivor's role."

"Oh, yes, Tamara knows that." Did Maclaren sound annoyed, as if his wife had been insulted? "We've both followed the reports of the study teams."

"No, wait, dear." Her fingers brushed across his. "I think Rero—Rero-and-Voah are trying to tell us how it *feels*." Her vision met ours. "Maybe we can tell you how it feels in us," she said. "Maybe that's part of the knowledge you're searching for."

She rose, crossed to where Rero sat, and squeezed the armored shoulder. Immediately realizing, she gave me the same gesture. "Would you like to see our children?" she asked. "There's the oldest, David's and mine. There are two more, Terangi's and mine. Will you believe that he loves them equally?"

Memory rushed over me of *The Adopted Son*. I have merely read it in translation. Somehow, though, across oceans and centuries, Hoiakim-and-Ranu's genius has come through to me. I think that from their poetry I know what it meant to live in a land where the nursing or pouching of an infant not one's own was not the highest form of devotion and sacrifice, but was actually taboo. It may be that from this I have an inkling of how deep goes the caring for our young.

Except . . .is this what she intends to say? I wondered.

"I wish you could cuddle them," Tamara said. "Well, they're asleep anyhow. You'll meet them properly tomorrow. What a gorgeous surprise for them!"

She activated a scanner to show us their rooms. I was touched and fascinated: the chubbiness of the small, the lengthening limbs of the oldest. Rero paid more heed to the adults. In our language she asked me, "Is my impression right, that in his mind they are secondary to her?"

"I have no idea," I confessed. "I'm wondering how they will feel about each other—the five of them—after the children are grown."

"And what is intrinsic, what cultural?"

"Impossible to say, darling. It could be that in them, parental emotions are potentiated by close association with the offspring, and in most human societies the mother enjoys more of this than the father does. ..."

The bit of intimacy went surprisingly far to ease things between us four. If we could not share smokeleaf, food, drink, odors, prayers, we could share parenthood. For a while Tamara was quite eagerly gossiping with Rero-and-me about our respective households. At last Maclaren said:

"Do you know, I suspect we may already be verging on an insight that's never been reached before." He paused; I saw him quiver where he sat. "Sure, sure, naturally we've gotten endless speculation on Earth, and doubtless on Arvel. How basic is the psychosexual element to any intelligent race? But it's been pretty dry and abstract. Here, tonight—well, we won't solve that problem, but might we not make a start on it? I've a wild guess as to how all your institutions, in all your cultures, may spring from your reproductive pattern. Might you be able to make a guess like that about us? It could tell us things about ourselves that've been mysterious through the whole of our history."

I thought for a span before I replied, "If nothing else, Terangi Maclaren, your guesses about us ought to reveal something about you."

He leaned forward. His hands made gestures. His tone held eagerness:

"With you people, the nuclear family—*really* nuclear—has got to be the basis of everything, everywhere and everywhen. It's the indissoluble unit . . . and I wish you could give me an idea of what the indissoluble unit is among humans.

"Your history, what little of it we know here on Earth—Never a nation-state. Usually clans, that might keep their identities for many centuries . . . forming tribes, that might keep their identities for a few centuries . . . but the families endure. They trace themselves back to mythic ages.

"More parochialism than on Earth, progress a local affair, few changes ever happening at once over your entire planet, obsolete and evil matters persisting till late dates in corners of the world. However, no nationalism; variety not getting ground down into uniformity; if nothing like democracy, then also nothing like absolutism; eventually, gradually, a union of the whole species on a loose and pragmatic foundation; no public passions, even for good causes, but no public lunacies either—

"In religion . . . when monotheism came along, God was bisexual—no, I suppose 'supersexual' would be a better word, but sexual for certain. At the same time, in everyday life, orderly sex relationships are the norm, taken for granted—therefore you don't have to worry about regulating that, you can make moral investments different from ours—"

The door flew open. A weapon came through.

Three men, likewise armed, crowded behind the automatic pistol of their leader. The whole group wore nondescript coveralls and hoods to mask their faces. Behind them I made out the raindrop shape of a little aircraft parked on the lawn. Engrossed in talk, we had none of us heard its whispering as anything but a night wind.

We sprang to our feet. "What the hell?" ripped from Maclaren.

"Vincent Indigo!" Rero-and-I cried together.

He was taken aback at our recognition of him. Unequipped for much conscious use of body language, humans are blind to countless details. He rallied at once, chopped air with his firearm, and snapped: "Silence. Not a peep out of you. The first that starts trouble, we'll shoot." A pause. "If you cooperate, nobody need get hurt. If you don't the kids might suffer too."

Tamara gasped and clutched at her husband. He laid an arm around her waist. Rero-and-I joined in a look of longing. We couldn't touch.

"We're taking the Arvelans away," Indigo said. "A kidnapping. The government ought to pay a fancy sum for their release. I'm telling you this so you'll see we don't mean worse and it's to your advantage to be good. Sir and Lady Maclaren, we're going to disable your phone and your car, to keep you from giving the alarm before we're a safe distance off. We don't want to do you more harm than that, and won't if you stand quietly where you are. As for you two . . . creatures, we don't want to harm you either. No ransom for a corpse, eh? We'll take care of you if you behave yourselves. If you don't—well,

a bullet doesn't need to kill you by itself. It only needs to make a hole in your sealsuit.

"Quiet, I said!" he ordered as Maclaren's mouth stirred. To his followers: "Get busy."

They grunted assent. One attacked the telephone. Not content to break its connection, he put a shot through the screen. The hiss of the pistol, the crack of splintered glass sounded louder than they were. He used the scanner to make sure the children had not roused, then rejoinded Indigo in keeping watch on us. Meanwhile his companions had gone back inside, evidently to the garage for their own task of demolition. I had noticed tools hung at their waists. This was a carefully planned operation.

Stupefaction left me; anger seethed up. *Vincent Indigo! The rest are unknowns — he must have left the official craft when it landed at a nearby airport to*

*wait for tomorrow, and met them —Was he always a
criminal, who slithered his way into public service,
or was it the chance he saw which corrupted him?*

No matter. He dares endanger Rero!

Beneath the fury, a logical part of me was baffled.
*His actions don't make sense. Probably he supposes,
probably rightly, that his name didn't register on the
Maclarens when we uttered it. Voice transponders
or no, we do have a thick accent. Nevertheless, can
he really hope that his part in this business will
remain hidden? He has to return us if he wants to
collect his price, and we'll denounce him —*

*Is he insane, to overlook that? Are his ac-
complices, too? He never struck me as irrational.
But what is sanity . . . in a human?*

My glance went to Maclaren and his wife. Over
the years I have learned in slight measure to read
expression, stance, aura in that race. Fear had
largely departed from them, now that it appeared
there was no direct physical threat. He stood
a-scowl with thought, and a cold wrath was coming
over him. She was regarding us, her guests, with a
horrified pity. Though they remained in bodily
contact, that was not where their attention lay.

It would have been for Rero-and-me, of course, if
we could have touched. But we could simply hold
gloves and make forlorn skin-signs.

The two men re-entered and reported their task
done. "Fine," Indigo said. "Let's get going. You"—
he pointed at the human prisoners—"stay indoors.
You"—that was us—"go on out."

The four kidnappers moved cautiously, two
ahead of us, two behind, while we shuffled forth.
Moonlight glimmered on early dew. The stars
looked infinitely far. The lights of the village and

of neighboring houses looked farther still. Most distant was the yellow glow from the home we had left.

Rero attempted speech in our language. Since our hosts could no longer hear it, Indigo did not forbid. Her words hurried: "Beloved, what do you suppose we should do? How can we trust them? They must be crazy to believe they can carry this off and go unpunished."

So her thought had paralled mine to that extent: hardly a surprise. Mine leaped onward. "No, they can reason, in a twisted fashion," I said. "Else they wouldn't have the kind of preparation and discipline they do. Perhaps they have a secure hiding place ready, or a change of identities, or whatever. The risk would still appear enormous to me — considering that we represent a whole planet, won't the Citadel bend every effort to hunting them down? — but what do we know of the ins and outs of Earth?" I clamped her fingers in mine, hard. "Best we stay calm, alert, bide our time. The ranson will surely be paid. If the Protector won't, then I expect those people who want alliance with our kind will subscribe to the sum demanded."

We reached the aircraft. Its door stood ajar above us. "Go on in," directed Indigo. His men drew closer.

We could not enter side by side in our bulky equipment. As it happened, I went first, climbing up a short extruded ladder. Cabin lighting was weak but sufficient. My gaze traveled aft, and I stopped short in the entrance.

"You have only one biostatic unit!" I protested. My hearts began to gallop. A roaring rose in my head.

"Yes, yes, we've no room for two," Indigo said impatiently. "Either of you can plug into it if you like. The other can last in his suit, or hers, till we get where we're bound. There we have an Arvel-conditioned chamber."

My look sought Rero's. Though her countenance was a blur in the moonlight, her aura throbbed red. Mine did too. She spoke in our language: "If that is true, why need they bother with a unit at all? They only mean to keep one of us alive. Not both."

"Alive as a hostage." My words sounded remote, a stranger's. "This is not a capture for money."

And rage took us into itself.

She at the thought that I might have to die, I at the thought that she might have to die, went aflame. You can imagine; but in these peaceful years of ours, you cannot know.

We were no longer persons, we were killing machines. Yet never had our awarenesses been more efficient. I believe I saw each dewdrop upon each blade of turf around the feet of those who would let Rero perish. I knew that my suit and its gear made me awkward, but I knew also that they were heavy. I gauged and sprang.

A man stood beside the ladder. My boots crashed on his skull. He went down beneath my mass, we rolled over, he lay broken, I lumbered up and charged at the next nearest. Rero was entangled with a third man Indigo danced about. He hadn't fired immediately for fear of hitting a comrade. He would in a moment, I knew, and Rero-and-I would be dead.

Dead together.

A form hurtled from the verandah, across the lawn, toward us. Utterly astounded, I did not slay him with whom I grappled. I only throttled him slack while I stared.

Maclaren. Maclaren had abandoned his wife to come help us.

He caught Indigo by surprise, from behind—grabbed the pistol wrist, threw his left arm around the man's neck, put a knee in the back.

I mastered myself and went to aid Rero. Despite her weight of apparatus, her small form was bounding back and forth, in and out, fast enough for her enemy to miss when he shot. Him I did pluck apart.

The moon stood higher when calm had returned to us. It had to the Maclarens earlier. In him it took the form of sternness, in her of a puzzled half-compassion, as we loomed above Vincent Indigo. He huddled in a chair, a blot upon that beautiful room, and pleaded with us.

"Certainly I'm going to take your flyer and fetch the police," Maclaren said. "But before then, in case the Citadel tries to cover for you, I want the facts myself." He realigned his audiovisual recorder. "Several copies of this tapel distributed in the right places—You were acting for the Protector, weren't you?"

Wretchedness stared back. "Please," Indigo whispered.

"Shall I break a few bones?" I asked.

"No!" Tamara exclaimed. "Voah, you can't talk that way. You're civilized!"

"He would have let Rero die, wouldn't he?" I retorted.

My wife's arm went around me. Through my sealsuit, I imagined the pressure, and the same desire kindled in us both. How long till we could

appease it? I heard the force she must use to stay reasonable as she counselled in our language: "Better we be discreet. Two men killed in a fight, that's condonable. But it wouldn't speak well for us, in human ears, if we injured helpless prisoners."

I subsided. "Correct," I said, "though does he need to know this?"

The spirit had gone out of Indigo anyhow. His aura flickered bluish-dim. He dropped his glance to the floor and mumbled, "Yes, that was the idea. Trying to make the Arvelans break off negotiations because they'd decide our race is too—oh, too unstable to be safe around. It couldn't be done officially, when so many dupes are putting on pressure for a treaty conference."

Maclaren nodded. "We were supposed to think it was the work of a criminal gang," he said. "Which it was indeed. A criminal gang in the Citadel, running the government. When that news breaks, I hope to see them not just out of office, but on trial."

"No!" Anguish whipped through Indigo. He raised eyes and hands, he shuddered. "You can't! Not the Protector—the *Dynasty*—God alive, Maclaren, can't you understand? That's what we've been trying to save. Would you let it crumble? Would you leave us defenseless before a pack of monsters?"

Silence grew until at last Maclaren said, from the bottom of his throat, "You actually believe that, don't you?"

"He does, he does," Tamara cried through tears. "Oh, the poor fool! Don't be too hard on him, Terangi. He was acting out of . . . out of love . . . wasn't he?"

Love, for such an object? Rero-and-I shared horror.

"I don't know as how that excuses him," Maclaren said grimly. "Well, we have his admission. Let the courts decide what to do with him and the rest. It won't matter."

He straightened, I saw him easing muscle by muscle, and he said to us: "What does matter is that the plot failed. I suppose there'll have to be a lot of behind-the-scenes bargaining, compromises, pretenses that certain individuals never were involved—political expediency. Not too important. What is important is that we can use the scandal to bring down the whole clique that's wanted to lock us up in a hermit kingdom. We will be leaguing with Arvel." Wonder trembled in his voice. "We truly will."

Truly? passed through Rero-and-me.

"Your doing!" Tamara hugged us both where we

stood. "If it hadn't been for your courage—"

"Why, there was no courage," Rero told her. "If we had gone meekly along, one of us would have died. What had we to lose?"

The knife that had formed within my soul flashed out of its sheath. "We would have been killed—which ought to have served the purpose reasonably well—if you had not intervened, Terangi Maclaren," I said, as if each word were being cut out of me.

He didn't notice my mood, in his pleasure, as he replied, "What else could I do, after the fighting began?" He hesitated. "It wasn't just your lives, Voah-and-Rero, though of course they meant a great deal. It was realizing that your race might well be provoked into withdrawing from ours. And that would have been about the most terrible loss humanity has ever had. Wouldn't it?"

"Your wife was endangered," I declared.

"I knew that," he said. They gripped hands, those two. Nevertheless he could tell me while she listened and nodded: "We both did. But we had the whole world to think about."

Rero-and-I do recommend making a pact, sharing transporter networks, conducting what trade and cultural exchange are possible. In our opinion, this will bring benefits outweighing any psychic harm of the kind that some fear. We can even suggest precautions to take against troublous influences.

Above all, O people of Arvel, never pity the beings on Earth. If you do, then sorrow will drown you. They know so little of love. They cannot ever know more. ●

SPIRALS

by Larry Niven
and Jerry Pournelle

The men and women
responsible for making
the world a better place
are not necessarily
<u>nice</u> people—
just indispensable.

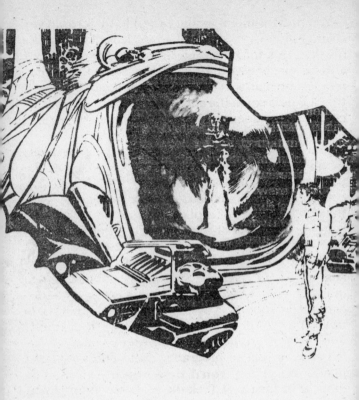

There are always people who want to revise history. No hero is so great that someone won't take a shot at him. Not even Jack Halfey.

Yes, I knew Jack Halfey. You may not remember my name. But in the main airlock of Industrial Station One there's an inscribed block of industrial diamond, and my name is sixth down: Cornelius L. Riggs, Metallurgist. And you might have seen my face at the funeral.

You *must* remember the funeral. All across the solar system work stopped while Jack Halfey took his final trek into the sun. He wanted it that way, and no spacer was going to refuse Jack Halfey's last request, no matter how expensive it might be. Even the downers got in the act. They didn't help pay the cost, but they spent hundreds of millions on sending reporters and cameras to the Moon.

That funeral damned near killed me. The kids who took me to the Moon weren't supposed to let the ship take more than half a gravity. My bones are over a hundred years old, and they're fragile. For that young squirt of a pilot the landing may have been smooth, but she hit a full gee for a second there, and I thought my time had come.

I had to go, of course. The records say I was Jack's best friend, the man who'd saved his life, and being one of the last survivors of the Great Trek makes me somebody special. Nothing would do but that I push the button to send Jack on his "final spiral into the sun", to quote a downer reporter.

I still see TriVee programs about ships "spiraling" into the sun. You'd think seventy years and more after the Great Trek the schools would teach kids something about space.

When I staggered outside in lunar gravity— lighter than the 20% gravity we keep in the Skylark, just enough to feel the difference—the reporters were all over me. Why, they demanded, did Jack want to go into the sun? Cremation and scattering of ashes is good enough for most spacers. It was good enough for Jack's wife. Some send their ashes back to Earth; some are scattered into the solar wind, to be flung throughout the universe; some

prefer to go back into the soil of a colony sphere. But why the sun?

I've wondered myself. I never was good at reading Jack's mind. The question that nearly drove me crazy, and did drive me to murder, was: why did Jack Halfey make the Great Trek in the first place?

I finally did learn the answer to that one. Be patient.

Probably there will never be another funeral like Jack's. The Big Push is only a third finished, and it's still two hundred miles of the biggest linear accelerator ever built, an electronic-powered railway crawling across the Earthside face of the Moon. One day we'll use it to launch starships. We'll fire when the Moon is full, to add the Earth's and Moon's orbital velocities to the speed of the starship, and to give the downers a thrill. But we launched Jack when the Moon was new, with precisely enough velocity to cancel the Earth's orbital speed of eighteen miles per second. It would have cost less to send him into interstellar space.

Jack didn't drop in any spiral. The Earth went on and the coffin stayed behind, then it started to fall into the Sun. It fell ninety-three million miles just like a falling safe, except for that peculiar wiggle when he really got into the sun's magnetic field. Moonbase is going to do it again with a probe. They want to know more about that wiggle.

The pilot was a lot more careful getting me home, and now I'm back aboard the Skylark, in a room near the axis where the heart patients stay; and on my desk is this pile of garbage from a history professor at Harvard who has absolutely proved that we would have had space industries and space colonies without Jack Halfey. There are no indispensible men.

In the words of a famous American president: Bullshit! We've made all the downers so rich that they can't remember what it was like back then.

And it was grim. If we hadn't got space industries established before 2020 we'd never have been able to afford them at all. Things were that thin. By 2020 A.D. there wouldn't have been any resources to invest. They'd have all gone into keeping eleven billion downers alive (barely!) and anybody who proposed "throwing money into outer space" would have been lynched.

God knows it was that way when Jack Halfey started.

I first met Jack Halfey at UCLA. He was a grad student in architecture, having got his engineering physics degree from Cal Tech. He'd also been involved in a number of construction jobs—among them Hale Observatory's big orbital telescope while he was still an undergrad at Cal Tech—and he was already famous. Everyone knows he was brilliant, and they're right, but he had another secret weapon: he worked his arse off. He had to. Insomnia. Jack couldn't sleep more than a couple of hours a night, and to get even that much sleep he had to get laid first.

I know about this because when I met Jack he was living with my sister. Ruthie told me that they'd go to bed, and Jack would sleep a couple of hours, and up he'd be, back at work, because once he woke up there was no point in lying in bed.

On nights when they couldn't make out he never went to bed at all, and he was pure hell to live with the next day.

She also told me he was one mercenary son of a bitch. That doesn't square with the public image of Jack Halfey, savior of mankind, but it happens to be true, and he never made much of a secret of it. He wanted to get rich fast. His ambition was to lie around Rio de Janeiro's beaches and sample the local wines and women; and he had his life all mapped out so that he'd be able to retire before he was forty.

I knew him for a couple of months, then he left UCLA to be a department head in the construction of the big Tucson arcology. There was a tearful scene with Ruthie: she didn't fit into Jack's image for the future, and he wasn't very gentle about how he told her he was leaving. He stormed out of her apartment carrying his suitcase while Ruthie and I shouted curses at him, and that was that.

I never expected to see him again.

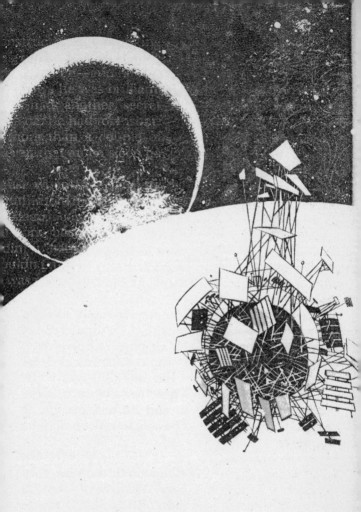

When I graduated there was this problem: I was a metallurgist, and there were a lot of us. Metallurgists had been in big demand when I started UCLA, so naturally everybody studied metallurgy and materials science; by the time I graduated it was damned tough getting a job.

The depression didn't help much either. I graduated right in the middle of it. Runaway inflation, research chopped to the bone, environmentalists and Only One Earthers and Friends of Man and the Earth and other such yo-yo's on the rise; in those days there was a new energy crisis every couple of years, and when I got my sheepskin we were in the middle of, I think, number 6. Industry was laying off, not hiring.

There was one job I knew of. A notice on the UCLA careers board. "Metallurgist wanted. High pay, long hours, high risk. Guaranteed wealthy in ten years if you live through it."

That doesn't sound very attractive just now, but in those days it looked better. Better than welfare, anyway, especially since the welfare offices were having trouble meeting their staff payrolls, so there wasn't a lot left over to hand out to their clients.

So, I sent in an application and found myself one of about a hundred who'd got past the paperwork screening. The interview was on campus with a standard personnel officer type who seemed more interested in my sports record than my abilities as a metallurgist. He also liked my employment history: I'd done summer jobs in heavy steel construction. He wouldn't tell me what the job was for.

"Not secret work," he said. "But we'd as soon not let it out to anyone we're not seriously interested in." He smiled and stood up, indicating the interview was over. "We'll let you know."

A couple of days later I got a call at the fraternity house. They wanted me at the Wilshire headquarters of United Space Industries.

I checked around the house but didn't get any new information. USI had contracts for a good bit of space work, including the lunar mines. Maybe that's it, I thought. I could hope, anyway.

When I got to USI the receptionist led me into a comfortable room and asked me to sit down in a big Eames chair. The chair faced an enormous TV screen (flat: TriVee wasn't common in those days. Maybe it was before TriVee at all; it's been a long time, and I don't remember). She typed something on an input console, and we waited a few minutes, and the screen came to life.

It showed an old man floating in mid-air.

The background looked like a spacecraft, which wasn't surprising. I recognized Admiral Robert McLeve. He had to be eighty or more, but he didn't look it.

"Good morning," he said.

The receptionist left. "Good morning," I told the screen. There was a faint red light on a lens by the screen, and I assumed he could see me as well as I could see him. "I'd kind of hoped for the Moon. I didn't expect the O'Neill colony," I added.

It took a while before he reacted, confirming my guess: a second and a half each way for the message, and the way he was floating meant zero gravity. I couldn't think of anything but the Construction Shack (that's what they called it then) that fit the description.

"This is where we are," McLeve said. "The duty tour is five years. High pay, and you save it all. Not

much to spend money on out here. Unless you drink. Good liquor costs like transplant rights on your kidneys. So does bad liquor, because you still have to lift it."

"Savings don't mean much," I said.

"True." McLeve grimaced at the thought. Inflation was running better than 20%. The politicians said they would have it whipped Real Soon Now, but nobody believed them. "We've got arrangements to have three quarters of your money banked in Swiss francs. If you go back early, you lose that part of your pay. We need somebody in your field, part time on the Moon, part time up here in the Shack. From your record I think you'd do. Still want the job?"

I wanted it all right. I was never a nut on the space industries bit—I was never a nut on anything—but it sounded like good work. Exciting, a chance to see something of the solar system (well, of near-Earth space and the Moon; nobody had gone further than that) as well as to save a lot of money. And with that job on my record I'd be in demand when I came home.

As to why me, it was obvious when I thought about it. There were lots of good metallurgists, but not many had been finalists in the Olympic gymnastics team trials. I hadn't won a place on the team, but I'd sure proved I knew how to handle myself. Add to that the heavy construction work experience and I was a natural. I sweated out the job appointment, but it came through, and pretty soon I was at Canaveral, strapping myself into a Shuttle seat, and having second and third thoughts about the whole thing.

There were five of us. We lifted out from the Cape in the Shuttle, then transferred in Earth orbit to a tug that wasn't a lot bigger than the old Apollo capsules had been. The trip was three days, and crowded. The others were going to Moon base. They refueled my tug in lunar orbit and sent me off alone to the Construction Shack. The ship was guided from the Shack, and it was scary as hell because there wasn't anything to do but wonder if they knew what they were doing. It took as long to get from the Moon to the Shack as it had to get to the Moon from Earth, which isn't surprising because it's the same distance: the Shack was in one of the stable libration points that make an equilateral triangle with the Earth and the Moon. Anything put there will stay there forever.

The only viewport was a small thing in the forward end of the tug. Naturally we came in ass-

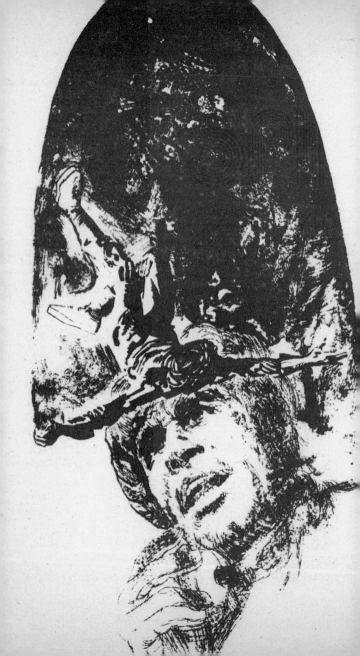

backwards so I didn't see much.

Today we call it the Skylark, and what you see as you approach is a sphere half a kilometer across. It rotates every two minutes, and there's all kinds of junk moored to the axis of rotation. Mirrors, the laser and power targets, the long thin spine of the mass driver, the ring of agricultural pods, the big telescope; a confusion of equipment.

It wasn't that way when I first saw it. The sphere was nearly all there was, except for a spiderweb framework to hold the solar power panels. The frame was bigger than the sphere, but it didn't look very substantial. At first sight the Shack was a pebbled sphere, a golf ball stuck in a spider's web.

McLeve met me at the airlock. He was long of limb, and startlingly thin, and his face and neck were a maze of wrinkles. But his back was straight, and when he smiled the wrinkles all aligned themselves. Laugh-lines.

Before I left Earth I read up on his history: Annapolis, engineer with the space program (didn't make astronaut because of his eyes); retired with a bad heart; wrote a lot of science fiction. I'd read most of his novels in high school, and I suppose half the people in the space program were pulled in by his stories.

When his wife died he had another heart attack. The Old Boys network came to the rescue. His classmates wangled an assignment in space for him. He hadn't been to Earth for seven years, and low gravity was all that kept him alive. He didn't even dare go to the Moon. A reporter with a flair for mythological phraseology called him "The Old Man of Space." It was certain that he'd never go home again, but if he missed Earth he didn't show it.

"Welcome aboard." He sounded glad to see me. "What do they call you?" he asked.

A good question. Cornelius might sound a dignified name to a Roman, but it makes for ribald comments in the USA. "Corky," I told him. I shrugged, which was a mistake: we were at the center of the sphere, and there wasn't any gravity at all. I drifted free from the grabhandle I'd been clinging to and drifted around the airlock.

After a moment of panic it turned out to be fun. There hadn't been room for any violent maneuvers in the tug, but the airlock was built to get tugs and rocket motors inside for repairs; it was big, nine meters across, and I could twirl around in the zero gravity. I flapped my arms and found I could swim.

McLeve was watching with a critical air. He must have liked what he saw because he grinned slightly. "Come on," he said. He turned in the air and drifted without apparent motion—it looked like levitation. "I'll show you around." He led the way out of the airlock into the sphere itself.

We were at the center of rotation. All around, above and below, were fields of dirt, some plowed, some planted with grass and grains.

There were wings attached to hooks at the entrance. McLeve took down a set and began strapping them on. Black bat wings. They made him look like a fallen angel, Milton's style. He handed me another pair. "Like to fly?" he asked.

I returned the grin. "Why not?" I hadn't the remotest idea of what I was doing, but if I could swim in the air with my hands, I ought to be able to handle wings in no gravity. He helped me strap in, and when I had them he gave some quick instructions.

"Main thing is to stay high," he said. "The further down the higher the gravity, and the tougher it is to control these things." He launched himself into space, gliding across the center of the sphere. After a moment I followed him.

I was a tiny chick in a vast eggshell. The landscape was wrapped around me: fields and houses, and layout yards of construction gear, and machinery, and vats of algae, and three huge windows opening on blackness. Every direction was down, millions of light years down when a window caught my attention. For a moment that was terrifying. But McLeve held himself in place with tiny motions of his wings, and his eyes were on me. I swallowed my fear and looked.

There were few roads. Mostly the colonists flew with their wings, flew like birds, and if they didn't need roads, they didn't need squared-off patterns for the buildings either. The "houses" looked like they'd been dropped at random among the green fields. They were fragile partitions of sheet metal (wood was far more costly than sheet steel here), and they could not have borne their own weight on Earth, let alone stand up to a stiff breeze. They didn't have to. They existed for privacy alone.

I wondered about the weather. Along the axis of the sphere I could see scores of white puffballs. Clouds? I gathered my courage and flapped my way over to the white patch. It was a flock of hens. Their feet were drawn up, their heads were tucked under their wings, and they roosted on nothing.

"They like it in zero gravity," McLeve said. "Only thing is, when you're below them you have to watch out."

He pointed. A blob of chicken splat had left the flock and moved away from us. It fell in a spiral pattern. Of course the splat was actually going in a straight line—we were the ones who were rotating, and that made the falling stuff look as if it were spiraling to the ground below.

"Automatic fertilizer machine," I said.

McLeve nodded.

"I wonder you don't keep them caged," I said.

"Some people like their sky dotted with fleecy white hens."

"Oh. Where is everybody?" I asked.

"Most are outside working," McLeve said. "You'll meet them at dinner."

We stayed at the axis, drifting with the air currents, literally floating on air. I knew already why people who came here wanted to stay. I'd never experienced anything like it, soaring like a bird. It wasn't even like a sail plane: you wore the wings and you flew with them, you didn't sit in a cockpit and move controls around.

There were lights along part of the axis. The mirrors would take over their job when they were installed; for the moment the lights ran off solar power cells plastered over the outside of the sphere. At the far end of the sphere was an enormous cloud of dust. We didn't get close to it. I pointed and looked a question.

"Rock grinder," McLeve said. "Making soil. We spread it over the northern end." He laughed at my frown. "North is the end toward the sun. We get our rocks from the Moon. It's our radiation shielding. Works just as well if we break it up and spread it around, and that way we can grow crops in it. Later on we'll get the agricultural compartments built, but there's always five times as much work as we have people to do it with."

They'd done pretty well already. There was grass, and millet and wheat for the chickens, and salad greens and other vegetable crops. Streams ran through the fields down to a ring-shaped pond at the equator. There was also a lot of bare soil that had just been put in place and hadn't been planted. The Shack wasn't anywhere near finished.

"How thick is that soil?" I asked.

"Not thick enough. I was coming to that. If you hear the flare warnings, get to my house. North pole."

I thought that one over. The only way to ward yourself from a solar flare is to put a lot of mass between you and the sun. On Earth that mass is a hundred miles of air. On the Moon they burrow ten meters into the regolith. The Shack had only the rock we could get from the Moon, and Moonbase had problems of its own. When they had the manpower and spare energy they'd throw more rock our way, and we'd plaster it across the outer shell of the Shack, or grind it up and put it inside; but for now there wasn't enough, and come flare time McLeve was host to an involuntary lawn party.

But what the hell, I thought. It's beautiful. Streams rushing in spirals from pole to equator. Green fields and houses, skies dotted with fleecy white hens; and I was flying as man flies in dreams.

I decided it was going to be fun, but there was one possible hitch.

"There are only ten women aboard," I said.

McLeve nodded gravely.

"And nine of them are married."

He nodded again. "Up to now we've mostly

needed muscle. Heavy construction experience and muscle. The next big crew shipment's in six months, and the company's trying like hell to recruit women to balance things off. Think you can hold out that long?"

"Guess I have to."

"Sure. I'm old navy. We didn't have women aboard ships and we lived through it."

I was thinking that I'd like to meet the one unmarried woman aboard. Also that she must be awfully popular. McLeve must have read my thoughts, because he waved me toward a big structure perched on a ledge partway down from the north pole. "You're doing all right on the flying. Take it easy and let's go over there."

We soared down, and I began to feel a definite "up" and "down"; before that any direction I wanted it to be was "up." We landed in front of the building.

"Combination mess hall and administration offices," McLeve said. "Ten percent level."

It took a moment before I realized what he meant. Ten percent level—ten percent of Earth's gravity.

"It's as heavy as I care to go," McLeve said. "And any lighter makes it hard to eat. The labs are scattered around the ring at the same level."

He helped me off with my wings and we went inside. There were several people, all men, scurrying about purposefully. They didn't stop to meet me.

They weren't wearing much, and I soon found that was the custom in the Shack; why wear clothes inside? There wasn't any weather. It was always warm and dry and comfortable. You mostly needed clothes for pockets.

At the end of the corridor was a room that hummed; inside there was a bank of computer screens, all active. In front of them sat a homely girl.

"Miss Hoffman," McLeve said. "Our new metallurgist, Corky Riggs."

"Hi." She looked at me for a moment, then back at the computer console. She was mumbling something to herself as her fingers flew over the keys.

"Dot Hoffman is our resident genius," McLeve said. "Anything from stores and inventories to orbit control, if a computer can figure it out she can make the brains work the problem."

She looked up with a smile. "We give necessity the praise of virtue," she said.

McLeve looked thoughtful. "Cicero?"

"Quintilian." She turned back to her console again.

"See you at dinner," McLeve said. He led me out.

"Miss Hoffman," I said.

He nodded.

"I suppose she wears baggy britches and blue wool stockings and that shirt because it's cool in the computer room," I said.

"No, she always dresses that way."

"Oh."

"Only six months, Riggs," the admiral said. "Well, maybe a year. You'll survive."

I was thinking I'd damned well have to.

I fell in love during dinner.

The chief engineer was named Ty Plauger, a long, lean chap with startling blue eyes. The chief ecologist was his wife, Jill. They had been married about a year before they came up, and they'd been aboard the Shack for three, ever since it started up. Neither was a lot older than me, maybe thirty then.

At my present age the concept of love at first sight seems both trite and incredible, but it was true enough. I suppose I could have named you reasons then, but I don't feel them now. Take this instead:

There were ten women aboard out of ninety total. Nine were married, and the tenth was Dot Hoffman. My first impression of her was more than correct. Dot never would be married. Not only was she homely, but she thought she was homelier still. She was terrified of physical contact with men, and the blue wool stockings and blouse buttoned to the neck were the least of her defenses.

If I had to be in love—and at that age, maybe I did—I could choose among nine married women. Jill was certainly the prettiest of the lot. Pug nose, brown hair chopped off short, green eyes, and a compact muscular shape, very much the shape of a woman. She liked to talk, and I liked to listen.

She and Ty had stars in their eyes. Their talk was full of what space would do for mankind.

Jill was an ex-Fromate; she'd been an officer in the Friends of Man and the Earth. But while the Fromates down below were running around sabotaging industries and arcologies and nuclear plants and anything else they didn't like, Jill went to space. Her heart bled no less than any for the baby fur seals and the three-spined stickleback and all the fish killed by mine tailings, but she'd thought of something to do about it all.

"We'll put all the dirty industries into space," she told me. "Throw the pollution into the solar wind and let it go out to the cometary halo. The Fromates think they can talk everyone into letting Kansas go back to buffalo grass—"

"You can't *make* people want to be poor," Ty put in.

"Right! If we want to clean up the Earth and save the wild things, we'll have to give people a way to get rich without harming the environment. This is it! Some day we'll send down enough power from space that we can tear down the dams and put the snail darter back where he came from."

And more. Jill tended to do most of the talking. I wondered about Ty. He always seemed to have the words that would set her off again.

And one day, when we were clustered around McLeve's house with, for a few restful hours, nothing to do, and Jill was well out of earshot flying around and among the chickens in her wonderfully graceful wingstyle, Ty said to me, "I don't *care* if we turn the Earth into a park. I like space. I like flying, and I like free fall, and the look of stars with no air to cloud them. But don't tell Jill."

I learned fast. With Ty in charge of engineering, McLeve as chief administrator, and Dot Hoffman's computers to simulate the construction and point up problems before they arose, the project went well. We didn't get enough mass from the Moon, so that my smelter was always short of raw materials, and Congress didn't give us enough money. There weren't enough flights from down below and we were short of personnel and goods from Earth. But we got along.

Two hundred and forty thousand miles below us, everything was going to hell.

First, the senior senator from Wisconsin lived long enough to inherit a powerful committee chairmanship, and he'd been against the space industries from the start. Instead of money we got "Golden Fleece" awards. Funds already appropriated for flights we'd counted on got sliced, and our future budgets were completely in doubt.

Next, the administration tried to bail itself out of the tax revolt by running the printing presses. What money we could get appropriated wasn't worth half as much by the time we got it.

Moonbase felt the pinch and cut down even more on the rock they flung out our way.

Ty's answer was to work harder: get as much of the Shack finished as we could, so that we could start sending down power.

"Get it done," he told us nightly. "Get a *lot* of it finished. Get so much done that even those idiots will see that we're worth it. So much that it'll cost them less to supply us than to bring us home."

He worked himself harder than anyone else, and Jill was right out there with him. The first task was to get the mirrors operating.

We blew them all at once over a couple of months. They came in the shuttle that should have brought our additional crew; it wasn't much of a choice, and we'd have to put off balancing out the sex ratio for another six months.

The mirrors were packages of fabric as thin as the cellophane on a package of cigarettes. We inflated them into great spheres, sprayed foam plastic on the outside for struts, and sprayed silver vapor inside where it would precipitate in a thin layer all over. Then we cut them apart to get spherical mirrors, and sliced a couple of those into wedges to mount behind the windows in the floor of the Shack.

They reflected sunlight in for additional crops.

Jill had her crew out planting more wheat to cut down on the supplies we'd need from Earth.

Another of the mirrors was my concern. A hemisphere a quarter of a kilometer across can focus a lot of sunlight onto a small point. Put a rock at that point and it melts, fast. When we got that set up we were all frantically busy smelting iron for construction out of the rocks. Moonbase shipped up when they could. When Moonbase couldn't fling us anything we dismounted rock we'd placed for shielding, smelted it, and plastered the slag back onto the sphere.

Days got longer and longer. There's no day or night aboard the Shack anyway, of course: open the mirrors and you have sunlight, close them and you don't. Still, habit dies hard, and we kept track of time by days and weeks; but our work schedules bore no relation to them. Sometimes we worked the clock around, quitting only when forced to by sheer exhaustion.

We got a shipment from Moonbase, and in the middle of the refining process the mounting struts in the big smelter mirror got out of alignment. Naturally Ty was out to work on it.

He was inspecting the system by flying around with a reaction pistol. The rule was that no one worked without a safety line; a man who drifted away from the Shack might or might not be rescued, and the rescue itself would cost time and manpower we didn't have.

Ty's line kept pulling him up short of where he wanted to go. He gave the free end to Jill and told her to pay out a lot of slack. Then he made a jump from the mirror frame. He must have thought he'd use the reaction pistol to shove him off at an angle so that he'd cross over the bowl of the mirror to the other side.

The pistol ran out of gas. That left Ty floating straight toward the focus of the mirror.

He shouted into his helmet radio, and Jill frantically hauled in slack, trying to get a purchase on him. I made a quick calculation and knew I would never reach him in time; if I tried I'd likely end up in the focus myself. Instead I took a dive across his back path. If I could grab his safety line, the jerk as I pulled up short ought to keep him out of the hottest area, and my reaction pistol would take us back to the edge.

I got the line all right, but it was slack. It had burned through. Ty went right through the hot point. When we recovered his body, metal parts on his suit had melted.

We scattered his ashes inside the sphere. McLeve's navy prayer book opened the burial service with the words "We brought nothing into this world, and it is certain that we shall take nothing out." Afterwards I wondered how subtle McLeve had been in his choice of that passage.

We had built this world ourselves, with Ty leading us. We had brought *everything* into this world, even down to Ty's final gift to us; the ashes which would grow grass in a place no human had ever thought to reach until now.

For the next month we did without him; and it was as if we had lost half our men. McLeve was a good engineer if a better administrator, but he couldn't go into the high gravity areas, and he couldn't do active construction work. Still, it wasn't engineering talent we lacked. It was Ty's drive.

Jill and Dot and McLeve tried to make up for that. They were more committed to the project than ever.

Two hundred and forty thousand miles down, they were looking for a construction boss. They'd find one, we were sure. We were the best, and we were paid like the best. There was never a problem with salaries. Salaries were negligible next to the other costs of building the Shack. But the personnel shuttles were delayed, and delayed again, and we were running out of necessities, and the US economy was slipping again.

We got the mirrors arrayed. Jill went heavily into agriculture, and the lunar soil bloomed, seeded with earthworms and bacteria from earthly soil. We smelted more of the rocky crust around the Shack and put it back as slag. We had plans for the metal we extracted, starting with a lab for growing metal whiskers. There was already a whisker lab in near-Earth orbit, but its output was tiny. The Shack might survive if we could show even the beginnings of a profit-making enterprise.

Jill had another plan: mass production of expensive biologicals, enzymes and various starting organics for ethical drugs.

We had lots of plans. What we didn't have was enough people to do it all. You can only work so many twenty-hour days. We began to make mistakes. Some were costly.

My error didn't cost the Shack. Only myself. I like to think it was due to fatigue and nothing more.

I made a try at comforting the grieving widow, after a decent wait of three weeks.

When Ty was alive everyone flirted with Jill. She pretended not to notice. You'd have to be crude as well as rude before she'd react.

This time it was different. I may not have been very subtle, but I wasn't crude; and she told me instantly to get the hell out of her cabin and leave her alone.

I went back to my refinery mirror and brooded.

Ninety years later I know better. Ninety years is too damned late. If I'd noticed nothing else, I should have known that nearly eighty unmarried men aboard would all be willing to comfort the grieving widow, and half of them were only too willing to use the subtle approach: "You're all that keeps us working so hard."

I wonder who tried before I did? It hardly matters; when my turn came, Jill's reaction was automatic. Slap him down before it's too late for him to back away. And when she slapped me down, I stayed slapped, more hurt than mad, but less than willing to try again.

I hadn't stopped being in love with her. So I worked at being her friend again. It wasn't easy. Jill was cold inside. When she talked to people it was about business, never herself. Her dedication to the Shack, and to all it stood for in her mind, was hardening, ossifying. And she spent a lot of time with Dot Hoffman and Admiral McLeve.

But the word came: another shuttle. Again there were no women. The Senator from Wisconsin had found out how expensive it would be to get us home. Add fifty women and it would be half again as expensive. So no new personnel.

Still they couldn't stop the company from sending up a new chief engineer, and we heard the shuttle was on its way, with a load of seeds, liquid hydrogen, vitamin pills, and Jack Halfey.

I couldn't believe it. Jack just wasn't the type.

To begin with, while the salary you could save in five years amounted to a good sum, enough to let you start a business and still have some income left, it wasn't *wealth*. You couldn't live the rest of your life in Rio on it; and I was pretty sure Jack's goals hadn't changed.

But there he was, the new boss. From the first day he arrived things started humming. It was the old Jack, brilliant, always at work, and always insisting everyone try to keep up with him although no one ever could. He worked our arses off. In two months he had us caught up on the time we lost after Ty was killed.

Things looked good. They looked damned good. With the mirrors mounted we could operate on sunlight, with spare power for other uses. Life from soil imported from Earth spread throughout the soil imported from the Moon; and earthly plants were in love with the chemicals in lunar soil. We planted strawberries, corn and beans together; we planted squashes and melons in low-gravity areas and watched them grow into jungles of thin vines covered with fruit.

The smelter worked overtime, and we had more than enough metals for the whisker lab and biological vats, if only a shuttle would bring us the pumps and electronics we needed; and if necessary we'd make pumps in the machine shops, and Jack had Dot working out the details of setting up integrated-circuit manufacture.

But the better things looked in space, the worse they looked on Earth.

One of the ways we were going to make space

colonies pay for themselves was through electricity. We put out big arrays of solar cells, monstrous spiderwebs a kilometer long by half that wide, so large that they needed small engines dotted all over them just to keep them oriented properly toward the sun.

We made the solar cells ourselves; one of the reasons they needed me was to get out the rare metals from the lunar regolith and save them for the solar-cell factory. And it was working; we had the structure and we were making the cells. Soon enough we'd have enormous power, megaWatts of power, enough to beam it down to Earth where it could pay back some of the costs of building the system. The orbiting power stations cost a fortune to put up, but not much to maintain; they would be like dams, big front end costs but then nearly free power forever.

We were sure that would save us. How could the United States turn down free electricity?

It looked good until the Fromates blew up the desert antenna that we would have been beaming the power down to, and the lawyers got their reconstruction tied into legal knots that would probably take five years to untangle.

The Senator from Wisconsin continued his crusade. This time we got *three* Golden Fleece awards. Down on Earth the company nominated him for membership in the Flat Earth Society. He gleefully accepted and cut our budget again.

We also had problems on board. Jack had started mean; it was obvious he had never wanted to come here in the first place. Now he turned mean as a rattlesnake. He worked us. If we could get the whisker lab finished ahead of time, at lower cost than planned, then maybe we could save the station yet; so he pushed and pushed again; and one day he pushed too hard.

It wasn't a mutiny. It wasn't even a strike. We all did a day's work; but suddenly, without as far as I know any discussion among us, nobody would put in overtime. Ten hours a day, yes; ten hours and one minute, no.

Jill pleaded. The Admiral got coldly formal. Dot cried. Jack screamed.

We cut work to nine and a half hours.

And then it all changed. One day Jack Halfey was smiling a lot. He turned polite. He was getting his two or three hours sleep a night.

Dot described him. "Like Mrs. Fezziwig," she said. " 'One vast substantial smile.' I hope she's happy. I wonder why she did it? To save the

Shack. . . ." She was trying to keep her voice cheerful, but her look was bitter. Dot wasn't naive; just terrified. I suppose that to her the only reason a woman would move in with a man would be to save some noble cause like the Shack.

As to Jill, she didn't change much. The Shack was the first step in the conquest of the universe, and it was by God going to be finished and self-sufficient. Partly it was a memorial to Ty, I think; but she really believed in what she was doing, and it was infectious.

I could see how Jack could convince her that he shared her goal. To a great extent he did, although it was pure selfishness; his considerable reputation was riding on this project. But Jack never did anything half-heartedly. He drove himself at whatever he was doing.

What I couldn't understand was why he was here at all. He must have *known* how thin were the chances of completing the Shack before he left Earth.

I had to know before it drove me nuts.

Jack didn't drink much. When he did it was often a disaster, because he was the world's cheapest drunk. So one night I plied him.

Night is generally relative, of course, but this one was real: the Earth got between us and the sun. Since we were in the same orbit as the Moon, but sixty degrees ahead, that happened to us exactly as often as there are eclipses of the moon on Earth; a rare occasion, one worth celebrating.

Of course we'd put in a day's work first, so the party didn't last long; we were all too beat. Still it was a start, and when the formalities broke up and Jill went off to look at the air system, I grabbed Jack and got him over to my quarters. We both collapsed in exhaustion.

I had brought a yeast culture with me from Canaveral. McLeve had warned me that liquor cost like diamonds up here; and a way to make my own alcohol seemed a good investment. And it was. By now I had vacuum distilled vodka made from fermented fruit bars and a mash of strawberries from the farm—they weren't missed; the farm covered a quarter of the inner surface now. My concoction tasted better than it sounds, and it wasn't hard to talk Jack into a drink, then another.

Presently he was trying to sing the verses to "The Green Hills of Earth." A mellower man you never saw. I seized my chance.

"So you love the green hills of Earth so much,

what are you doing here? Change your mind about Rio?"

Jack shook his head; the vibration ran down his arm and sloshed his drink. "Nope . . ." Outside a hen cackled, and Jack collapsed in laughter. "Let me rest my eyes on the fleecy skies . . ."

Grimly I stuck to the subject. "I thought you were all set with that Tucson arcology."

"Oh, I was. I was indeed. It was a *beautiful* setup. Lots of pay, and—" He stopped abruptly.

"And other opportunities?" I was beginning to see the light.

"Welllll . . . yes. But you have to see it the way I did. First, it was a great opportunity to make a name for myself. A city in a building! Residential and business and industry all in the same place, one building to house a quarter . . . of a million . . .

people. And it would have been beautiful, Corky. The plans were magnificent! I was in love with it. Then I got into it, and I saw what was really going on.

"Corky, everyone was stealing that place blind! The first week I went to the chief engineer to report shortages in deliveries and he just looked at me. 'Stick to your own work, Halfey,' says he. Chief engineer, the architects, construction bosses, even the catering crew—every one of them was knocking down twenty-five, fifty percent! They were selling the cement right off the boxcars and substituting sand. There wasn't enough cement in that concrete to hold up the walls."

"So you took your share."

"Don't get holy on me! Dammit, look at it my way. I was willing to play square, but they wouldn't let me. The place was going to fall down. The weight of the first fifty thousand people would have done it. What I could do was make sure nobody got inside before it happened." Jack Halfey chortled. "I'm a public benefactor, I am. I sold off the reinforcing rods. The inspectors couldn't possibly ignore that."

"Nothing else?" I asked.

"Wellll, those rods were metal-whisker compote. Almost as strong as diamond, and almost as expensive. I didn't need anything else. But I made sure they'd never open that place to the public. Then I stashed my ill-gotten gains and went underground and waited for something to happen."

"I never heard much about it. Of course, I wouldn't, up here."

"Not many down there heard either. Hush hush while the FBI looked into it. The best buy I ever made in my life was a subscription to the *Wall*

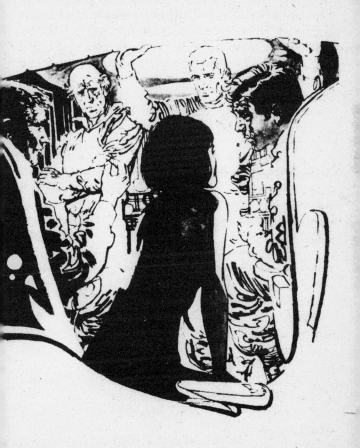

Street Journal. Just a paragraph about how the Racket Squad was investigating Mafia involvement in the Tucson arcology. That's when things fell into place."

I swung around to refill his glass, carefully. We use great big glasses, and never fill them more than half full. Otherwise they slosh all over the place in the low gravity. I had another myself. It was pretty good vodka, and if I felt it, Jack must be pickled blue. "You mean the building fell in?"

"No, no. I realized why there was so *much* graft." Jack sounded aggrieved. "There was supposed to be graft. I wasn't supposed to get in on it."

"Aha."

"Aha you know it. I finished reading that article on a plane to Canaveral. The FBI couldn't follow me to Rio, but the Mafia sure could. I'd heard there was a new opening for chief engineer for the Construction Shack, and all of a sudden the post looked very, very good."

He chuckled. "Also, I hear that things are tightening up in the USA. Big crackdown on organized crime. Computer-assisted. Income tax boys and Racket Squad working together. It shouldn't be long before all the chiefs who want my arse are in jail. Then I can go back, cash my stash, and head for Rio."

"Switzerland?"

"Oh, no. Nothing so simple as that. I thought of something else. Say, I better get back to my bunk." He staggered out before I could stop him. Fortunately it was walking distance from my place to his; if he'd had to fly, he'd probably have ended up roosting with the chickens.

"Bloody hell," says I to myself.

Should I add that I had no intention of robbing Jack? I was just curious: what inflation-proof investment had he thought up? But I didn't find out for a long time . . .

A month later the dollar collapsed. Inflation had been a fact of life for so long that it was the goal of every union and civil service organizer to get inflation written into their contracts, thereby increasing inflation. The government printed money faster to compensate: more inflation. One of those vicious spirals. Almost suddenly, the dollar was down the drain.

There followed a full-scale taxpayer revolt.

The Administration got the message: they were spending too much money. Aha! Clearly that had to stop. The first things to go were all the projects that wouldn't pay off during the current President's term of office. Long term research was chopped out of existence. Welfare, on the other hand, was increased, and a comprehensive National Health Plan was put into effect, even though they had to pay the doctors and hospitals in promissory notes.

The Senator from Wisconsin didn't even bother giving us his customary Golden Fleece Award. Why insult the walking dead?

We met in our usual place, a cage-work not far from the north pole. Admiral McLeve was in the center, in zero gravity. The rest of us perched about the cage-work, looking like a scene from Hitchcock's *The Birds*.

Dot had a different picture, from Aristophanes. "Somewhere, what with all these clouds and all this air, There must be a rare name, somewhere . . . How do you like Cloud-Cuckoo-Land?

Putting on wings does things to people. Halfey had dyed his wings scarlet, marked with yellow triangles enclosing an H. Dot wore the plumage of an eagle, and I hadn't believed it the first time I saw it; it was an incredibly detailed, beautiful job. McLeve's were the wings of a bat, and I tell you he looked frightening, as evil as Dracula himself. Leon Briscoe, the chemist, had painted mathematical formulae all over his, in exquisite medieval calligraphy. Jill and Ty had worn the plumage of male and female Least Terns, and she still wore hers. There were no two sets of wings alike in that flock. We were ninety birds of ninety species, all gathered as if the ancient roles of predator and prey had been set aside for a larger cause. Cloud-Cuckoo-Land.

A glum Cloud-Cuckoo-Land.

"It's over," McLeve said. "We've been given three

months to phase out and go home. Us, Moonbase, the whole space operation. They'll try to keep some of the near-Earth operations going a while longer, but we're to shut down."

Nobody said anything at first. We'd been expecting it, those of us who'd had time to follow news from Earth. Now it was here, and nobody was ready. I thought about it: back to high gravity again. Painful.

And Jill. Her dream was being shot down. Ty died for nothing. Then I remembered McLeve. He wasn't going anywhere. Any gravity at all was a death sentence.

And I hated Jack Halfey for the grin he was hiding. There had been a long piece in the latest newscast about the roundup of the Mafia lords; grand juries working overtime, and the District of Columbia jail filled, no bail to be granted. It was safe for Jack down there, and now he could go home early.

"They can't do this to us!" Jill wailed. A leftover Fromate reflex, I guess. "We'll—" Go on strike? Bomb something? She looked around at our faces, and-when I followed the look I stopped with Dot Hoffman. The potato face was withered in anguish, the potato eyes were crying. What was there for Dot on Earth?

"What a downer," she said.

I almost laughed out loud, the old word was so inadequate. Then McLeve spoke in rage. "Downers. Yes. Nine billion downers sitting on their fat arses while their children's future slides into the muck. Downers is what they are."

Now you know. McLeve the wordsmith invented that word, on that day.

My own feelings were mixed. Would the money

stashed in Swiss francs be paid if we left early, even though we had to leave? Probably, and it was not a small amount; but how long would it last? There was no job waiting for me . . . but certainly I had the reputation I'd set out for. I shouldn't have much trouble getting a job.

But I like to finish what I start. The Shack was *that* close to being self-sufficient. We had the solar power grids working. We even had the ion engines mounted all over the grid to keep it stable. We didn't have the microwave system to beam the power back to Earth, but it wouldn't be that expensive to put in . . . except that Earth had no antennae to receive the power. They hadn't even started reconstruction. The permit hearings were tied up in lawsuits.

No. The Shack was dead. And if our dollars were worthless, there were things that weren't. Skilled labor *couldn't* be worthless. I would get my francs, and some of my dollar salary had been put into gold. I wouldn't be broke. And—the clincher— there were women on Earth.

McLeve let us talk a while. When the babble died down and he found a quiet lull, he said, very carefully, "Of course, we have a chance to keep the station going."

Everyone talked at once. Jill's voice came through loudest. "How?"

"The Shack was designed to be a self-sufficient environment," McLeve said. "It's not quite that yet, but what do we need?"

"Air," someone shouted.

"Water," cried another.

I said, "Shielding. It would help to have enough mass to get us through a big solar flare. If they're shutting down Moonbase we'll never have it."

Jill's voice carried like a microphone. "Rocks? Is that all we need? Ice and rocks? We'd have both in the asteroid belt." It was a put-up job. She and McLeve must have rehearsed it.

I laughed. "The Belt is two hundred million miles away. We don't have ships that will go that far, let alone cargo . . . ships . . ." And then I saw what they had in mind.

"Only one ship," McLeve said. "The Shack itself. We can move it out into the Belt."

"How long?" Dot demanded. Hope momentarily made her beautiful.

"Three years," McLeve said. He looked thoughtful. "Well, not quite that long."

"We can't live three years," I shouted. I turned to Jill, trusting idiot that I was then. "The air system can't keep us alive that long, can it? Not enough chemicals—"

"But we can do it!" she shouted. "It won't be easy, but the farm is growing now. We have enough plants to make up for the lack of chemical air purification. We can recycle everything. We've got the raw sunlight of space. Even out in the asteroids that will be enough. We can do it."

"Can't hurt to make a few plans," McLeve said.

It couldn't help either, thought I; but I couldn't say it, not to Dot and Jill.

II

These four were the final architects of The Plan: Admiral McLeve, Jill Plauger, Dot Hoffman, and

Jack Halfey.

At first the most important was Dot. Moving something as large as the Shack, with inadequate engines, a house in space never designed as a ship; that was bad enough. Moving it farther than any manned ship, no matter the design, should have been impossible.

But behind that potato face was a brain tuned to mathematics. She could solve any abstract problem. She knew how to ask questions; and her rapport with computers was a thing to envy.

Personal problems stopped her cold. Because McLeve was one of the few men she could see as harmless, she could open up to him. He had told me sometime before we lost Ty, "Dot tried sex once and didn't like it." I think he regretted saying even that much. Secrets were sacred to him. But for whatever reason, Dot couldn't relate to people; and that left all her energy for work.

Dot didn't talk to women either, through fear or envy or some other reason I never knew. But she did talk to Jill. They were fanatical in the same way. It wasn't hard to understand Dot's enthusiasm for The Plan.

McLeve had no choices at all. Without the Shack he was a dead man.

Jack was in the Big Four because he was needed. Without his skills there would be no chance at all. So he was dragged into it, and we watched it happen.

The day McLeve suggested going to the asteroids, Jack Halfey was thoroughly amused, and showed his mirth to all. For the next week he was not amused by anything whatever. He was a walking temper tantrum. So was Jill. I expect he tried to convince her that with sufficient wealth, exile on Earth could be tolerable. Now he wasn't sleeping, and we all suffered.

Of course our miseries, including Jack's, were only temporary. We were all going home. All of us.

Thus we followed the downer news closely, and thus was there a long line at the communications room. Everyone was trying to find an Earthside job. It hardly mattered. There was plenty of power for communications. It doesn't take much juice to close down a colony.

We had no paper, so the news was flashed onto a TV for the edification of those waiting to use the transmitter. I was waiting for word from Inco: they had jobs at their new smelter in Guatemala. Not the world's best location, but I was told it was a tropical paradise, and the quetzal was worth at least as much as the dollar.

I don't know who Jack was expecting to hear from. He looked like a man with a permanent hangover, except that he wasn't so cheerful.

The news, for a change, wasn't all bad. Something for everyone. The United States had issued a new currency, called "marks" (it turns out there were marks in the US during revolutionary times); they were backed by miniscule amounts of gold.

Not everyone was poor. Technology proceeded apace. Texas Instruments announced a new pocket computer, a million bits of memory and fully programmable, for twice what a calculator cost. Firestone Diamonds—which had been manufacturing flawless bluewhite diamonds in a laboratory for the past year, and which actually was owned by a man named Firestone—had apparently swamped the engagement ring market, and was now making chandeliers. A diamond chandelier would cost half a year's salary, of course, but that was expected to go down.

The "alleged Mafia chieftains" now held without bail awaiting trial numbered in the thousands. I was surprised: I hadn't thought it would go that far. When the dollar went worthless, apparently Mafia bribe money went worthless too. Maybe I'm too cynical. Maybe there was an epidemic of righteous wrath in government.

Evidently someone thought so, because a bond issue was approved in California, and people were beginning to pay their taxes again.

Something for everyone. I thought the Mafia item would cheer Jack up, but he was sitting there staring at the screen as if he hadn't seen a thing and didn't give a damn anyway. My call was announced and I went in to talk to Inco. When I came out Jack had left, not even waiting for his own call. Lack of sleep can do terrible things to a man.

I wasn't surprised when Jack had a long talk with McLeve, nor when Jill moved back in with him. Jack would promise anything, and Jill would believe anything favorable to her mad scheme.

The next day Jack's smile was back, and if I thought it was a bit cynical, what could I do? Tell Jill? She wouldn't have believed me anyway.

They unveiled The Plan a week later. I was invited to McLeve's house to hear all about it.

Jack was there spouting enthusiasm. "Two problems," he told us. "First, keeping us alive during the trip. That's more Jill's department, but what's the problem? The Shack was designed to last centuries. Second problem is getting out there. We've got that figured out."

I said, "The hell you do. This isn't a spaceship, it's just a habitat. Even if you had a, a big rocket motor to mount on the axis, you wouldn't have fuel for it, and if you did, the Shack would break up under the thrust." I hated him for what he was doing to Jill, and I wondered why McLeve wasn't aware of it. Maybe he was. The admiral never let anyone know what he thought.

"So we don't mount a big rocket motor," Jack said. "What we've got is just what we need: a lot of little motors on the solar panels. We use those and everything else we have. Scooters and tugs, the spare panel engines, and, last but not least, the Moon. We're going to use the Moon for a gravity sling."

He had it all diagrammed out in four colors. "We shove the Shack toward the Moon. If we aim just right, we'll skim close to the lunar surface with everything firing. We'll leave the Moon with that velocity plus the Moon's orbital velocity, and out we go."

"How close?"

He looked to Dot. She pursed her lips. "We'll clear the peaks by two kilometers."

"That's close."

"More than a mile," Jack said. "The closer we come the faster we leave."

"But you just don't have the thrust!"

"Almost enough," Jack said. "Now look. We keep the panel thrusters on full blast. That gives us about a quarter percent of a gravity, not *nearly* enough to

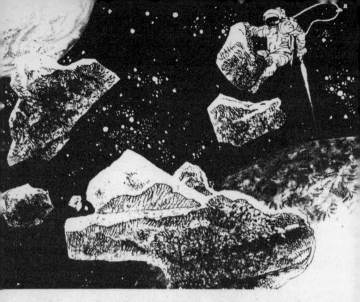

break up the Shack, Corky. And we use the mirrors." He poked buttons and another diagram swam onto McLeve's drafting table. "See."

It showed the Shack with the window mirrors opened all the way for maximum surface area. My smelter mirror was hung out forward. Other mirrors had been added. "Sails! Light pressure adds more thrust. Not a lot, but enough to justify carrying their mass. We can get to the Belt."

"You're crazy," I informed them.

"Probably," McLeve muttered. "But from my viewpoint it looks good."

"Sure. You're dead anyway, no offense intended. We're playing a game here, and it's getting us nowhere."

"I'm going." Jill's voice was very low and very convincing. It stirred the hair on my neck.

"Me too," Dot added. She glared at me, the

enemy.

I made one more try. They'd had more time to think about it than I did, but the thrust figures were right there, scrawled in an upper corner of the diagram. "Now pay attention. You can't possibly use the attitude jets on the solar panels for that long. They work by squirting dust through a magnetic field, throwing it backward so the reaction pushes you forward. Okay, you've got free solar power, and you can get the acceleration. But where can you possibly get enough dust?" I saw Jack's guilty grin, and finished, "Holy shit!"

Jack nodded happily.

"Why not?" Jill asked. "We won't need solar flare shielding around Ceres. On the way we can keep what we do have between us and the Sun, while we grind up the surplus."

They meant it. They were going to make dust out of the radiation shields and use that.

In theory it would work. The panel engines didn't care what was put through them; they merely charged the stuff up with electricity gathered from the solar cells and let the static charge provide the push. A rocket is nothing more than a way to squirt mass overboard; any mass will do. The faster you can throw mass away, the better your rocket.

At its simplest a rocket could be a man sitting in a bucket throwing rocks out behind him. Since a man can't throw very fast that wouldn't be a very good rocket, but it would work.

But you have to have rocks, and they were planning on using just about all of ours.

It was a one-way mission. They'd have to find an

asteroid, and fast, when they got to the Belt; by the time they arrived they'd be grinding up structure, literally taking the Shack apart, and all that would have to be replaced.

It would have to be a special rock, one that had lots of metal, and also had ice. This wasn't impossible, but it wasn't any sure thing either. We knew from Pioneer probes that some of the asteroids had strata of water ice, and various organics as well; but we couldn't tell which ones. We knew one more thing from the later probes, and The Plan was geared to take advantage of that.

The Skylark—newly named by McLeve, and I've never known why he called it that—would head for Ceres. There were at least three small-hill-sized objects orbiting that biggest of the asteroids.

A big solar flare while they were out that far would probably kill the lot of them. Oh, they had a safety hole designed: a small area of the Shack to huddle inside, crowded together like sardines, and if the flare didn't last too long they'd be all right—

Except that it would kill many of the plants needed for the air supply.

I didn't think the air recycling system would last any three years either, but Jill insisted it was all right.

It didn't matter. I wasn't going, and neither was Jack; it was just something to keep Jill happy until the shuttle came.

There was more to The Plan. All the non-essential personnel would go to Moonbase, where there was a better chance. Solar flares weren't dangerous to them. Moonbase was buried under twenty feet of lunar rock and dust. They had lots of mass. There's oxygen chemically bound in lunar rock, and if you have enough power and some hydrogen you can bake it out. They had power: big solar mirrors, not as big as ours, but big. They had rocks. The hydrogen recycles if it's air you want. If you want water, the hydrogen has to stay in the water.

We figured they could hang on for five years.

Our problem was different. If Moonbase put all its effort into survival, they wouldn't have the resources to keep sending us rocks and metal and hydrogen. Hydrogen is the most abundant element in the universe; but it's rare on the Moon. Without hydrogen you don't have water. Without water you don't have life.

I had to admit things were close. We were down to a shuttle load a month from Earth; but we needed those. They brought hydrogen, vitamins, high-protein foods. We could grow crops; but that took water, and our recycling systems were nowhere near 100% efficient.

Now the hydrogen shipments had stopped. At a cost of fifty million dollars a flight before the dollar collapsed, the USA would soon stop sending us ships!

Another thing about those ships. They had stopped bringing us replacement crew long ago. Jack was the last. Now they were taking people home. If they stopped coming, we'd be marooned.

A few more years and we could be self-sufficient. A few more years and we could have colonists, people who never intended to go home. They were aboard now, some of them. Jill and Ty, before Ty was killed. Dot Hoffman was permanent. So was McLeve, of course. Of the seventy-five still

aboard—we'd lost a few to the shuttles—twenty-five or so, including all the married couples, thought of themselves as colonists.

The rest of us wanted to go home.

Canaveral gave us fifty days to wind up our affairs. The shuttles would come up empty but for the pilots, with a kind of sardine-can-with-seats fitted in the hold.

I could understand why McLeve kept working on The Plan. Earth would kill him. And Jill: Ty's death had no meaning if the Shack wasn't finished. Dot? Sure. She was valuable, here.

But would you believe that I worked myself stupid mounting mirrors and solar panel motors? It wasn't just for something to do before the shuttle arrived, either: I had a nightmare living in my mind.

McLeve was counting on about twenty crew: the Big Four, and six of the eight married couples, and

116   *DESTINIES*

up to half a dozen additional men, all held by their faith in The Plan.

The history books have one thing right. The Plan was Jack Halfey's. Sure, Jill and McLeve and Dot worked on it, but without him it couldn't be brought off. Half of the Plan was no more than a series of contingency operations, half-finished schemes that relied on Halfey's ingenuity to work. McLeve and Halfey were the only people aboard who really knew the Shack—knew all its parts and vulnerabilities, what might go wrong and how to fix it; and McLeve couldn't do much physical work. He wouldn't be outside working when something buckled under the stress.

And there would be stress. A hundredth of a gravity doesn't sound heavy, but much of our solar panel area and all our mirrors were flimsy as tissue paper.

Without Halfey it wouldn't, couldn't work. When Halfey announced that he was going home on that final shuttle, the rest would quit too. They'd beg the downers for one more shuttle, and they'd get it, of course, and they'd hold the Shack until it came.

But McLeve couldn't quit, and Dot wouldn't, and I just couldn't be sure about Jill. If Halfey told her he wasn't really going, would she see reason? The son of a bitch was trading her life for a couple of hours sleep. When Skylark broke from orbit, would she be aboard? She and Dot and the Admiral, all alone in that vast landscaped bubble with a growing horde of chickens, going out to the asteroids to die. The life support system might last a long time with only three humans to support: they might live for years.

So I worked. When they finally died, it wouldn't be because Cornelius Riggs bobbled a weld.

The first shuttle came and picked up all non-essential personnel. They'd land at Moonbase, which was the final staging area for taking everyone home. If the plan went off as McLeve expected, many of them would be staying on the Moon, but they didn't have to decide that yet.

I was classed as essential, though I'd made my intentions clear. The Plan needed me: not so much on the trip out, but when they reached the Belt. They'd have to do a lot of mining and refining, assuming they could find the right rock to mine and refine.

I let them talk me into waiting for the last shuttle. I wouldn't have stayed if I hadn't known Halfey's intentions, and I confess to a squirmy feeling in my guts when I watched that shuttle go off without me.

The next one would be for keeps.

When you have a moral dilemma, get drunk. It's not the world's best rule, but it is an old one: the Persians used the technique in classical times. I tried it.

Presently I found myself at McLeve's home. He was alone. I invited myself in.

"Murdering bastard," I said.

"How?"

"Jill. That crazy plan won't work. Halfey isn't even going. You know it and I know it. He's putting Jill on so she won't cut him off. And without him there's not even a prayer."

"Your second part's true," McLeve said. "But not the first. Halfey is going."

"Why would he?"

McLeve smirked. "He's going."

"What happens if he doesn't?" I demanded. "What then?"

"I stay." McLeve said. "I'd rather die here than in a ship."

"Alone?"

He nodded. "Without Halfey it is a mad scheme. I wouldn't sacrifice the others for my heart condition. But Halfey isn't leaving, Corky. He's with us all the way. I wish you'd give it a try too. We need you."

"Not me."

How was Halfey convincing them? Not Jill: she wanted to believe in him. But McLeve, and Dot—

Dot had to know. She had to calculate the shuttle flight plan, and for that she had to know the masses, and the total payload mass for that shuttle had to equal all the personnel except McLeve but including the others.

Something didn't make any sense.

I waited until I saw eagle wings and blue wool stockings fly away from the administration area, and went into her computer room. It took a while to bring up the system, but the files directory was self-explanatory. I tried to find the shuttle flight plan, but I couldn't. What I got, through sheer fumbling, was the updated flight plan for the Skylark.

Even with my hangover I could see what she'd done: it was figured for thirty-one people, plus a mass that had to be the shuttle. Skylark would be carrying a captain's gig . . .

The shuttle was coming in five days.

Halfey had to know that shuttle wouldn't be taking anyone back. If he wasn't doing anything about it, there was only one conclusion. He was going to the Belt.

A mad scheme. It doomed all of us. Jill, myself, Halfey, myself—

But if Halfey didn't go, no one would. We'd all go home in that shuttle. Jill would be saved. So would I.

There was only one conclusion to that. I had to kill Jack Halfey.

How? I couldn't just shoot him. There wasn't anything to shoot him with. I thought of ways. Put a projectile into a reaction pistol. But what then? Space murder would delight the lawyers, and I might even get off; but I'd lose Jill forever, and without Halfey . . .

Gimmick his suit. He went outside regularly. Accidents happen. Ty wasn't the only one whose ashes we'd scattered into the soil of the colony.

Stethoscope and wrench: stethoscope to listen outside the walls of Halfey's bed chamber, a thoroughly frustrating and demeaning experience; but presently I knew they'd both be asleep for an hour or more.

It took ten minutes to disassemble Jack's hose connector and substitute a new one I'd made up. My replacement looked just like the old one, but it wouldn't hold much pressure. Defective part. Metal fatigue. I'd be the one they'd have examine the connector if there was any inquiry at all. And I had no obvious motive for killing Jack; just the opposite, except for Jill and McLeve I was regarded as Jack's only friend.

Once that was done I had only to wait.

The shuttle arrived empty. Halfey went outside,

all right, but in a sealed cherry picker; he wasn't exposed to vacuum for more than a few moments, and apparently I'd made my substitute just strong enough to hold.

They docked the shuttle, but not in the usual place, and they braced it in.

It was time for a mutiny. I wasn't the only one being Shanghaied on this trip. I went looking for Halfey. First, though, I'd need a reaction pistol. And a projectile. A ball-point pen ought to do nicely. Any court in the world would call it self-defense.

"I'm a public benefactor, I am," I muttered to myself.

Jill's quarters were near the store room. When I came out with the pistol, she saw me. "Hi," she said.

"Hi." I started to go on.

"You never talk to me any more."

"Let's say I got your message."

'That was a long time ago. I was upset. So were you. It's different now . . ."

"Different. Sure." I was bitter and I sounded it. "Different. You've got that lying bastard Halfey to console you, that's how it's different." That hurt her, and I was glad of it.

"We need him, Corky. We all need him, and we always did. We wouldn't have got much done without him."

"True enough—"

"And he was driving all of you nuts, wasn't he? Until I—helped him sleep."

"I thought you were in love with him."

She looked sad. "I like him, but no, I'm not in love with him." She was standing in the doorway of her quarters. "This isn't going to work, is it? The Plan. Not enough of you will come. We can't do it, can we."

"No." Might as well tell her the truth. "It never would have worked, and it won't work now even if all of us aboard come along. Margin's too thin, Jill. I wish it would, but no."

"I suppose you're right. But I'm going to try anyway."

"You'll kill yourself."

She shrugged. "Why not? What's left anyway?" She went back into her room.

I followed. "You've got a lot to live for. Think of the baby fur seals you could save. And there's always me."

"You?"

"I've been in love with you since the first time I saw you."

She shook her head sadly. "Poor Corky. And I treated you just like all the others, back then when—. I wish you'd stay with us."

"I wish you'd come back to Earth with me. Or even Moonbase. We might make a go of Moonbase. Hang on until things change down there. New administration. Maybe they'll want a space program, and Moonbase would be a good start. I'll stay at Moonbase if you'll come."

"Will you?" She looked puzzled, and scared, and I wanted to take and hold her. "Let's talk about it. Want a drink?"

"No, thank you."

"I do." She poured herself something. "Sure you won't join me?"

"All right."

She handed me something cold, full of shaved ice. It tasted like Tang. We began to talk, about life on Earth—or even on Moonbase. She mixed us more drinks, Tang powder and water from a pitcher and vodka and shaved ice. Presently I felt good. Damned good.

One thing led to another, and I was holding her, kissing her, whispering to her—

She broke free and went over to close and lock her door. As she came back toward me she was unbuttoning the top of her blouse.

And I passed out.

When I woke I didn't know. Now, ninety years later, I still don't. For ninety years it has driven me nuts, and now I'll never know.

All that's certain is that I woke half dressed, alone in her bed, and her clothes were scattered on the deck. I had a thundering hangover and an urgent thirst. I drank from the water pitcher on her table—

It wasn't water. It must have been my own 100 proof vodka. Next to it was a jar of Tang and a bowl that had held shaved ice—and a bottle holding more vodka. She'd been feeding me vodka and Tang and shaved ice.

No wonder I had a hangover worthy of being bronzed as a record.

I went outside. There was something wrong.

The streams weren't running correctly. They stood at an angle. At first I thought it was me. Then they sloshed.

The Shack was under acceleration.

There were a dozen others screaming for blood outside the operations building. One was a stranger—the shuttle pilot. The door was locked, and Halfey was talking through a loudspeaker.

"Too late," he was saying. "We don't have enough

thrust to get back to the L-4 point. We're headed for the Belt, and you might as well get used to the idea. We're going."

There was a cheer. Not everyone hated the idea. Eventually those who did understood: Halfey had drained the shuttle fuel and stored it somewhere. No escape that way.

No other shuttles in lunar orbit. Nothing closer than Canaveral, which was days away even if there were anything ready to launch. Nothing was going to match orbits with us.

We were headed for the Moon, and we'd whip around it and go for the Belt, and that was as inevitable as the tides.

When we understood all that they unlocked the doors.

An hour later the alarms sounded. "Outside. Suit up. Emergency outside!" McLeve's voice announced.

Those already in their suits went for the airlocks. I began half-heartedly putting on mine, in no hurry. I was sure I'd never get my swollen, pulsing head inside the helmet.

Jack Halfey dashed past, suited and ready. He dove for the airlock.

Halfey. The indispensible man. With a defective connector for an air intake.

I fumbled with the fasteners. One of the construction people was nearby and I got his help. He couldn't understand my frantic haste.

"Bastards kidnapped us," he muttered. "Let them do the frigging work. Not me."

I didn't want to argue with him, I just wanted him to hurry.

A strut had given way, and a section of the solar panel was off center. It had to be straightened, and we couldn't turn off the thrust while we did it. True, our total thrust was tiny, a quarter of a percent of a gravity, hardly enough to notice, but we needed it all.

Because otherwise we'd go out toward the Belt but we wouldn't get there, and by the time the Shack—Skylark, now—returned inevitably to Earth orbit there'd be no one alive aboard her.

I noticed all the work, but I didn't help. Someone cursed me, but I went on, looking for Halfey.

I saw him. I dove for him, neglecting safety lines, forgetting everything. I had to get to him before that connector went.

His suit blew open across the middle. As if the fabric had been weakened with, say, acid. Jack screamed and tried to hold himself together.

He had no safety line either. When he let go he came loose from the spiderweb. Skylark pulled away from him, slowly, two and a half centimeters per second per second; slow but inexorable.

I lit where he'd been, turned, and dove for him. I got him and used my reaction pistol to drive us toward the airlock.

I left it on too long. We were headed fast for the airlock entrance, too fast, we'd hit too hard. I tumbled about to get Jack across my back so that I'd be between him and the impact. I'd probably break a leg, but without Halfey I might as well have a broken neck and get it over with.

Leon Briscoe, our chemist, had the same idea. He got under us and braced, reaction pistol flaring behind us. We hit in a *menage à trois*, with me as Lucky Pierre.

Leon cracked an ankle. I ignored him as I threw
Halfey into the airlock and slammed it shut, hit the
recycle switch. Air hissed in.

Jack had a nosebleed, and his cough sounded
bad; but he was breathing. He'd been in vacuum
about forty seconds. Fortunately the decompres-
sion hadn't been totally explosive. The intake line
to his suit had fractured a half second before the
fabric blew . . .

The Moon grew in the scopes. Grew and kept
growing, until it wasn't a sphere but a circle, and
still it grew. There were mountains dead ahead.

"How close?" I demanded.

Dot had her eyes glued to a radar scope. "Not too
close. About a kilometer."

"A *kilometer*!" One thousand meters. "You said
two, before."

"So I forgot the shuttle pilot." She continued to stare at the scope, then her fingers bashed at the console keyboard. "Make that 800 meters," she said absently.

I was past saying anything. I watched the Moon grow and grow. Terror banished the last of my hangover; amazing what adrenalin in massive doses can do.

Jill looked worse than I did. And I didn't know. Were we lovers?

"Thirty seconds to periastron," Dot said.

"How close?" McLeve asked.

"Five hundred meters. Make that four-fifty."

"Good," McLeve muttered. "Closer the better."

He was right; the nearer we came to the Moon, the more slingshot velocity we'd pick up, and the faster we'd get to the Belt.

"Periastron," Dot announced. "Closest approach, four twenty-three and a fraction." She looked up in satisfaction. Potato eyes smiled. "We're on our way."

III

On Earth we were heroes. We'd captured the downers' imaginations. Intrepid explorers. Before we were out of range we got a number of offers for book rights, should we happen to survive.

There were even noises about hydrogen shipments to the Moon. Of course there was nothing they could do for us. There weren't any ships designed for a three-year trek.

Certainly Skylark wasn't. But we were trying it.

There were solar flares. We all huddled around McLeve's house, with as much of our livestock as we could catch stuffed into his bedroom. It took weeks to clean it out properly afterward. We had to re-seed blighted areas and weed out mutated plants after each flare. More of our recycled air was coming from the algae tanks now.

In a time of the quiet sun we swarmed outside and moved all of the mirrors. The sun was too far away now, and the grass was turning brown, until we doubled the sunlight flooding through the windows.

But it seemed we'd reach Ceres. Already our telescopes showed five boulders in orbit around that largest of the asteroids. We'd look at them all, but we wanted the smallest one we could find: the least daunting challenge. If it didn't have ice somewhere in its makeup, the next one would, or the next.

And then we'd all be working like sled dogs, for our lives.

I was circling round the outside of Skylark, not working, just observing: looking for points with some structural strength, places where I could put stress when the real work began. Win or lose, with or without a cargo, we would have to get home a lot faster than we came. The life support system wouldn't hold up forever. Something would give out. Vitamins, water, something in the soil or the algae tanks. Something.

Our idea was to build a mass driver, a miniature of the machine that had been throwing rocks at us from the Moon. If we found copper in that rock ahead—a pinpoint to the naked eye now, near the tiny battered disk of Ceres—we could make the kilometers of copper wire we'd need. If not, iron would do. We had power from the sun, and dust from the rocks around Ceres, and we'd send that dust down the mass driver at rocket-exhaust speeds. Home in ten months if we found copper.

I went back inside.

The air had an odd smell when I took off my helmet. We were used to it; we never noticed now unless we'd been breathing tanked air. I made a mental note: mention it to Jill. It was getting stronger.

I had only the helmet off when Jean and Kathy Gaynor came to drag me out. I was clumsy in my pressure suit, and they thought that was hilarious. They danced me around and around, pulled me out into the grass, and began undressing me with the help of a dozen others.

It looked like I'd missed half of a great party. What the hell, Ceres was still a week away. They took my pressure suit off and scattered the components, and I didn't fight. I was dizzy and had the giggles. They kept going. Presently I was stark naked and grabbing for Kathy, who took to the air before I realised she had wings. I came down in a stream and surfaced still giggling.

Jack and Jill were on their backs in the grass, watching the fleecy white hens and turning occasionally to avoid chicken splat. I liked seeing Jill so relaxed for once. She waved, and I bounced over and somersaulted onto my back next to them.

A pair of winged people were way up near the axis, flapping among the chickens, scaring them into panic. It was like looking into Heaven, as you find it painted on the ceilings of some of the European churches. I couldn't tell who they were.

"Wealth comes in spirals too," Jill was saying in a

dreamy voice. I don't think she'd noticed I wasn't wearing clothes. "We'll build bigger ships with the metal we bring home. Next trip we'll bring back the whole asteroid. One day the downers will be getting all their metal from us. And their whisker compotes, and drugs, and magnets, and, and free-fall alloys. Dare I say it? We'll own the world!"

"I said, "Yeah." There were puffball chickens drifting down the sky, as if they'd forgotten how to fly.

"There won't be anything we can't do. Corky, can you see a mass driver wrapped all around the Moon? For launching starships. The ships will go round and round. We'll put the mag—mag, net, ic levitation plates overhead, to hold the ships down after they're going too fast to stay down."

Halfey said, "What about a hotel on Titan? Excursions into Saturn's rings. No downers allowed."

"We'll spend our second honeymoon there," said Jill.

"Yeah," I said, before I caught myself.

Halfey laughed like hell. "No, no, I want to build it!"

I was feeling drunk and I hadn't had a drink. Contact high, they call it. I watched those two at the axis as they came together in a tangle of wings, clung together. Objects floated around them, and presently began to spiral outward, fluttering and tumbling. I recognized a pair of man's pants.

It made me feel as horny as hell. Two hundred million miles away there was a planet with three billion adult women. Out of that number there must be millions who'd take an astronaut hero to their beds. Especially after I published my best-selling memoirs. I'd never be able to have them all,

but it was certainly worth a try. All I had to do was go home.

Hah. And Thomas Wolfe thought *he* couldn't go home again!

A shoe smacked into a nearby roof, and the whole house *bonged*. We laughed hysterically. Something else hit almost beside my head: a hen lay on her back in the wheat, stunned and puzzled. The spiral of clothing was dropping away from what now seemed a single creature with four wings. A skinny blue snake wriggled out of the sky and touched down. I held it up, a tangle of blue wool. "My God!" I cried. "It's Dot!"

Jill rolled over and stared. Jack was kicking his heels in the grass, helpless with laughter. I shook my head; I was still dizzy. "What *have* you all been drinking? Not that Tang mixture again!"

Jill said, "Drinking?"

"Sure, the whole colony's drunk as lords," I said. "Hey . . . black wings . . . is that *McLeve* up there?"

Jill leapt to her feet. "Oh my God," she screamed. "The air!"

Jack bounded up and grabbed her arm. "What's happened?"

She tried to pull away. "Let me go! It's the air system. It's putting out alcohols. Not just ethanol, either. We're all drunk and hypoxic. Let me go!"

"One moment." Jack was fighting it and losing. In a moment he'd collapse in silliness again. "You knew it was going to happen," he said. His voice was full of accusation.

"Yes," Jill shouted. "Now will you let me go?"

"How did you know?"

"I knew before we started," Jill said. "Recycling isn't efficient enough. We need fresh water. Tons of fresh water."

"If there's no ice on that rock ahead—"

"Then we probably won't get to another rock," Jill said. "*Now* will you let me go work on the system?"

"Get out of here, you bitch," Jack yelled. He pushed her away and fell on his face.

It was scary. But there was also the alcohol. Fear and anger and ethanol and higher ketones and God knows what else fought it out in my brain. Fear lost.

"She's kept it going with Kleenex and bubble gum," I shouted. "And you believed her. When she told you it'd last three years. You believed." I whooped at the joke.

"Oh, shut up," Jack shouted.

"We've had it, right?" I asked. "So tell me something. Why did you do it? I was *sure* you were putting Jill on. I *know* you intended to go with the shuttle. So why?"

"Chandeliers," Jack said.

"Chandeliers?"

"You were there. Firestone Gems will sell you flawless blue-whites. A chandelier of them for the price of half a year's salary."

"And—"

"What the fuck do you think I did with my stash?" Jack screamed.

Stash. His ill-gotten gains from the Mafia. Stashed as blue-white diamonds.

Funny. Fun-nee. So why wasn't I laughing?

Because the bastard had kidnapped me, that's why. When he found his stash was worthless and he wasn't rich, and he'd probably face a jail term he couldn't bribe his way out of, he'd run as far away as a man could go. And taken me with him.

I crawled over to my doorway. My suit lay there in a sprawl. I fumbled through it to the equipment belt.

"What are you doing?" Halfey yelled.

"You'll see." I found the reaction pistol. I went through my pockets, carefully, until I found a ball-point pen.

"Hey! No!" Jack yelled.

"I'm a public benefactor, I am," I told him. I took aim and fired. He tumbled backwards.

* * *

There are always people who want to revise history. No hero is so great that someone won't take a shot at him. Not even Jack Halfey.

Fortunately I missed. ●

NEW BEGINNINGS

COMES THE REVOLUTION, COMRADES

by
J.E. POURNELLE
PH.D.

> "We're going to make it,
> we're going to demonstrate
> the scientific possibility
> of fusion."

This isn't the column Jim Baen and I had intended for this month. Some time ago, when we were both at another magazine, we conceived the notion of a column on "How to become a space colonist," and that was what we'd hoped to give you this month. Unfortunately an old Greek lady named Catastrophe intervened.

Larry Niven and I hike; and generally we take a troop of Boy Scouts. This year we'd planned a 50 miles 6-day hike in the High Sierra, and the boys have been training for it all year. This final training hike was several miles up the Iron Fork of the San Gabriel river, which went without incident until, on the way back, we paused for a swim; and while I was getting into the stream I fell and broke my right hand.

Nothing particularly serious. I can testify that the plastic bottle containing the sun protection "Blockout" works well as an emergency splint for the third and fourth metacarpals if you're ever so unfortunate as to need one; I can also testify that first-aid courses should emphasize the importance of removing all rings in cases of fracture: they had to saw off my ring when we reached the hospital. They also turned my hand into a lump of plaster attached to an elbow, making it impossible to type more than ten words per minute.

Worse, notes I make with my left hand turn out to be only slightly easier to read than Linear A. Thus I was unable to do the necessary research for the space-colonist article—and what little I did left no legible tracks. And when, cast and all, I duly attended our long-planned 50-miler I returned to be confronted by the deadline for this column.

Fortunately my computer makes it *possible* to write one-handed, although it's a bit tiring and not very fast; but you'll have to be satisfied with a different column from the one we'd hoped for.

* * *

There were several interesting items in the news

awaiting me on my return from the Sierra. The first is of personal interest: *LUCIFER'S HAMMER* by Larry Niven and Jerry Pournelle is still on the best-seller list. The second has a more universal appeal, although it contains a hooker that's a bit frightening. In my paper it was buried back on page nine, so it's possible some readers missed it; it went this way:

"STEP REPORTED TO LIMITLESS POWER
The Washington Post

WASHINGTON—The attainment of a temperature of 60 million degrees for half a second in a Princeton University laboratory was described Monday as the first step toward a limitless supply of electricity for the world.

"We're going to make it, we're going to demonstrate the scientific feasibility of fusion," Dr. Melvin B. Gottlieb, director of Princeton's Plasma Physics Laboratory said at a press conference held at the Department of Energy. Gottlieb said a demonstration of fusion could occur as early as 1981 or 1982 when the Tokamak Fusion Test Reactor under construction at Princeton will begin to operate. . . .

John M. Deutch, director of energy research for the Department of Energy, cautioned Monday that the Princeton achievement did not change the national timetable for the commercial production of electricity from fusion."

Hopeful news, eh? Gottlieb went on to say that it took seven years to go from 5 million degress to 25 million, and only six months to reach 60 million. Calling a few other experts around the country confirmed what seemed obvious: this was a real breakthrough; a rapid advance that hadn't been anticipated.

Moreover, it's an advance others may not have for a while. Although the Soviets are known to be forging ahead in fusion research, Dr. Gerald Yonas, fusion project manager at Sandia, says he'd be much surprised to learn that the Soviets have the neutral beam technology used at Princeton. We will, he says, be able to study high-temperature plasmas, and the Princeton achievement "speaks to the whole prospect of how rapidly we can bring in a new technology and apply it to physics. It wasn't long ago that we were playing with kiloVolt temperature."

Sounds hopeful, doesn't it? But note that last paragraph in the news article.

The breakthrough "does not change the national timetable." Does that seem curious? Here we have an unexpected achievement, something of great importance to engineering physics as well as a capability of prolonged study of phenomena (high temperature plasmas) which formerly were only mathematical concepts—but it doesn't change the national timetable.

Of course it doesn't: there is no national timetable for the commercial production of electricity from fusion. The expected date for US fusion power is never, and thus no breakthrough will bring it closer.

In 1965, 12.6 cents of every dollar spent by government went to support scientific inquiry. The result was to build a great pool of talent and knowledge that we are now exploiting: the US had a near monopoly on Nobel Prizes in 1977; the sports sections of the newspapers advertise computers available to anyone; we have wonder drugs, digital watches, new health care techniques, plenty to eat. A plethora of wonders pour forth for our enjoyment. Almost all of them are a direct result of our prior investments in science and technology.

In 1975, we spent only 5.7 cents of each government dollar on science. Nor is industry picking up the slack: in 1976 industry put $38 billion into all aspects of R&D, most for exploitation of discoveries made 10 to 15 years ago. Measured in constant dollars this is a 5% drop from 1968.

At this rate we may well see another newspaper story one day:

"FINAL PLANS FOR REACTOR DELIVERY
Reuters
TOKYO— OFFICIALS of Mitsubishi confirmed today that final contracts have been signed between Mitsubishi and Westinghouse under which Westinghouse will provide support personnel for installation of the Mitsubishi-designed fusion reactor to be installed in Ensenada.

Although the reactor design is by Mitsubishi, the scientific breakthroughs which made controlled fusion possible resulted from work by US research teams, work that was later terminated for lack of funds.

Under previous contract arrangements with Southern California Edison, San Diego Power and Light, and the Los Angeles Department of Water and Power, Mitsubishi will construct the reactor in Mexico and sell the resulting electric power to California. A substantial fee will be paid to Mexico for allowing reactor construction and the arrangement with Mexico must be renegotiated after ten years. In addition to construction costs, Mitsubishi will receive an inflation-adjusted fee based on the number of kiloWatts produced by the reactor.

Mon. March 25, 1987"

All made up, of course, but might it not happen? At the moment we pay the incredible sum of $50 billion a year for foreign energy, when it's fairly obvious that no more than $50 billion invested in space research a few years ago would save at least half that forever; continue with the same lack of foresight and we could well end paying the Mexicans and Japanese similar amounts—with similar disastrous effects on the dollar—to get fusion energy even if it's our technology. After all—the oil technology is ours, too.

Fat lot of good it does us.

But nothing lasts forever. True, the current administration seems enamoured of "soft energies", the kind you get by working your individual can off forking up manure or climbing about on the roof of your house (at least one study has estimated the danger of solar power, per kiloWatt, to be about ten times that of coal and fifty times that of nuclear, and the large number of people who'd have to climb on roofs is not a negligible part of the hazard); true there seems to be a conspiracy of the intellectuals to condemn *any* energy technology that might actually work, so that we may soon expect the intelligentsia to "discover" the hidden dangers in fusion power; but administrations change, and the American people obviously have faith in our engineers and scientists.

In fact, that's probably Carter's major problem with his energy proposals. He wants us to make do, cut back, use less: to put high taxes on energy in order to force conservation. The American people simply don't believe him. Somewhere, they reason, there is a good hardheaded Yankee (probably with a Slavic or Jewish name) working away in his basement, and before the crunch gets serious he"ll trot out a method for producing all we want. Haven't we always done things that way?

The American people don't *want* conservation. We like our big cars and air conditioning, and we think we deserve them.

And "deserve" them or not, we can have them—if we're willing to invest in the future. The investment need not be very large. Less than we spend on booze or cigarettes or cosmetics, and we don't even need to give up drinking and smoking and primping to get the investment funds.

Suppose we make the effort: either through a change in Congress and administration or a change of heart on the part of those in office, we make the investments. Where might we go, and when?

* * *

The first is implied by Dr. Gottfried: breakeven by 1982. For the benefit of readers not familiar with fusion reactors, I'd better explain.

Einstein postulated that $e = mc^2$: matter and energy, far from being different kinds of entities, are simply two different states of the same "thing", and can be converted one to the other. From that equation came the work of Fermi and his "pile" in the squash court at the University of Chicago; that proved the theory. A more dramatic proof came later with Trinity and Hiroshima, and some years after that came controlled nuclear power.

All this works by fission: a heavy nucleus, such as Uranium 235 or Plutonium 238 is hit just right by a neutron; the nucleus splits to form two new elements, often barium and krypton. However, if you add up the weights of the fission products, you'll find they total less than the mass of the original atom. Some of the mass has been "lost" — it has become energy.

Fusion works the other way. A light element, such as hydrogen, is literally squeezed until its atoms collapse together to form something heavier, such as helium. Ths mass of the result is a bit less than that of the original hydrogen, and the difference has been converted to energy.

Sounds easy but it's not; the reaction requires enormous temperatures. At 100 million degrees K the hydrogen you're trying to fuse gets active and wants OUT; you've got to hold it in place long enough for the reaction.

There are two ways to accomplish this. One is simply to squeeze the stuff: but there's no material known that can stand those temperatures. The reactor walls will melt long before the reaction can happen. So? Use non-material walls. A magnetic bottle, for example. While you're at it, make the ends of the "bottle" a magnetic field as well, ending with a doughnut-shaped reactor, the best-known of which is called a "Tokamak" (from a Russian acronym). An early type of Tokamak was used at Princeton to achieve the latest breakthrough, and they're hoping that when they get the full-sized reactor they'll get out more energy from fusion than they put in as heat and electricity to generate the magnetic field.

A second method is "inertial confinement": instead of holding the fusion "fuel" in place for a long time, confine it in tiny pellets and zap it from all sides at once; if you hit it with enough energy the reaction will start and will itself confine the fuel long enough to get energy back out. Things you might zap the pellet with are laser beams, as at Rochester and Livermore and Los Alamos, or electrons and protons as at Gerald Yonas's shop in Sandia.

The inertial confinement programs are moving along, if a bit jerkily. Although he didn't tell me this, I happen to know that Yonas spends about as much time in Washington trying to keep his budget—his program has been cancelled and restarted half a dozen times in the past three years—as he does in the lab trying to make neutrons. At Livermore, where they're building a big glass laser, and at Los Alamos where they're constructing an enormously powerful CO_2 laser, the story's more or less the same: they get their funds, but only after a big fight that consumes a lot of time better put into science and which scares the livers out of the junior scientists, who don't know if they'll have jobs next year or not no matter how successful their work may be.

It wasn't long ago fusion was pure theory: unlike fission which was demonstrated, fusion was theoretically possible but required not mere engineering, but scientific breakthroughs. That's not so true now: it's a very good bet that fusion can be made to work. How long it takes is something else again, for the moment the only workable nuclear power system is old reliable fission. (And the only alternative to fission over the next twenty years is coal.)

Now we could run the country on fission power, but there are problems. Fission requires expensive fuels, and in fact it's worse than that, because only a tiny fraction of the uranium—itself a rare enough element—that we mine is the right kind of stuff to fission. The rest has to be converted. We know how to do that but the process is expensive, and it's messy as well, producing various radioactive wastes which, although not all that hard to take care of compared to the wastes from coal, aren't trivial either. There's also the problem that fission fuels can without too much ingenuity be used to make bombs, and so it's legitimate to worry about how many nations will join the nuclear club.

No one deep-down believes that fission power is more than a means to get us to the next century. We're lucky to have it, and in my judgment we have insufficiently exploited our nuclear capabilities. But nobody really loves fission; it will always be rather expensive and require expensive fuels.

Though the future looks bright, the situation with fusion is complex. At the moment the only thing we can get to fuse are isotopes of hydrogen: Deuterium and Tritium.

Deuterium is more or less readily available from seawater: for every 6000 atoms of hydrogen in "normal" water there is one molecule of "heavy water" containing an atom of Deuterium, and the cost of separating it out is relatively trivial: a water main only 50 cm (20 inches) in diameter would supply enough Deuterium to generate the entire world's energy needs.

Tritium, however, is a bit harder to get. It is very rare in nature, and must in general be "bred" by bombarding lithium with neutrons. Lithium is not so rare as to be a limiting factor in the use of fusion, but it isn't common as dirt either.

Moreover, Tritium is dangerous stuff that you don't really want leaking out to the atmosphere, but being nothing more than ordinary hydrogen with two extra neutrons, it's slippery and hard to keep.

The reason for all this attention to Deuterium and Tritium is that we can get a Deuterium-Tritium reaction going at about 100 million degrees, and a Deuterium-Deuterium reaction at not impossibly higher temperatures; while a pure hydrogen fusion reaction (such as takes place in the Sun) requires temperatures and pressures beyond our wildest dreams. Maybe in a hundred years these limits will seem silly, but for now we're stuck with the heavy isotopes of hydrogen.

Fortunately Deuterium (one extra neutron in a hydrogen atom; call it D) and Tritium (T) are vastly cheaper—per kiloWatt/hour of power produced—than uranium, coal or oil. Given now-predictable temperatures and pressures we can liberate so much energy from D and T that it takes only a few grams to produce the energy needed by each of us for a whole year. Contrast that to about ten tons of coal needed per each man, woman, and child (10 billion tons a year for the US alone before the end of the century) and you'll see the advantage. Fusion really does hold out the promise of unlimited power forever.

There are problems, though. For one thing, D-T fusion delivers its energy in the form of fast neutrons, just as fission does. Those neutrons have to be stopped somehow in order to make use of their energy. In practice this is done by surrounding the reactor with a blanket thick enough to absorb the neutrons; and whenever you bombard anything with neutrons you'll get some unwanted radioactive byproducts. Proper design of the reactor blanket—part of it will have to be lithium to breed Tritium—can cut the radioactive wastes to a minimum, but there's no way to eliminate them entirely. Thus we'll have to give thought to what to do with these wastes.

Not that this is anything to worry about from an engineer's view. At the very worst they can be stuck out onto the Mojave Desert and covered with concrete. For that matter, so could the radioactive wastes from present-day fission plants. (Two hundred years' worth wouldn't fill the Superbowl). Despite the scare myths you hear (nuclear wastes remain radioactive for a million years!) the fact is that even fission wastes, after about 600 years, are less radioactive than the natural ore mined to get uranium. But there must be a system to deal with fusion wastes—and we don't have one. Furthermore, the system must be politically as well as scientifically acceptable—and that may take a while.

Thus my pessimism. We could have a scientific fusion reactor by 1983, and a commercial demonstration reactor by 1988; but we probably won't. The political reality is that given permit hearings (it takes over 60 different licenses and permits to start up a nuclear power plant!), interventions by every "concerned" group you can think of, lawyers getting rich by stuffing their briefcases into the works, and all the rest, we probably can't even get a site *selected* in less than seven to nine years. Thus we ought to be starting now the cumbersome process of site selection and approval if we want fusion power before the end of the century.

And make no mistake: as fusion becomes scientifically possible it will become the target for many who now claim to want it. It will come as a complete and disappointing surprise to a number of environmentalists that fusion will produce nuclear wastes. Suddenly we'll need many more studies, endless studies; there will be demonstrations and disruptions; and fusion will have as many political problems as fission has now.

In fact, one of the items on my desk after my return from the hike was Richard Geis's newsletter (Richard E. Geis, Personal Journal, Box 11408, Portland OR 97211; a highly uninhibited and personal journal of opinions, mostly libertarian; $3.00 for 5 issues). He too had read the news item about the fusion breakthrough, and had this to say in comment:

"But the thing that bothers me is those incredible temperatures bottled in a strong magnetic field.

"What happens if the magnetic 'bottle' breaks at the wrong time? Is there an explosive expansion of all that contained heat? Given a commercial-size 'bottle' that fails . . . would the released heat melt the facility . . . start fires in the countryside? Create strong air vector currents which would affect local weather? Release harmful gasses from vaporized equipment into the air?

"These are fears and speculations at the moment. Having a 'bottled sun' in the same country—even the same state—does not turn me on. And you can imagine the scare tactics that could be used by the opponents of fusion power. (And there will be opponents—ideological, religious, commercial—who will fear or stand to lose from the introduction of fusion power."

Now if Geis, a reasonable man who is NOT a knee-jerk opponent of technology and cheap power, can raise such worries, imagine what's going to happen when the professional "Amerika Stinks" and "technology is evil" crowd get into the act in a few years.

To answer Richard's objections: what happens if the "magnetic bottle" containing the fusion reaction breaks?

First, understand something: the problem with fusion is not to prevent "runaway reactions", it's to keep the reaction going. The plasma (a very hot ionized gas) in a magnetic confinement reactor is actually very thin, a low-grade industrial vacuum. When it is heated the plasma gets energetic, and the moving charged particles *themselves create magnetic fields*. Thus the flow of gas is unstable, and the gas often "gets loose" and touches the walls of the reactor. In addition, the neutrons released by the reaction blast off molecules from the reactor walls, and these get into the plasma. In both cases the effect is the same: the extra matter poisons the reaction, the plasma cools off, and *the reaction stops*.

Thus, the effect of the bottle "breaking" is to stop the reaction

What about all that tremendous heat stored inside? First of all, unlike fission reactors (which have relatively low temperatures but enormous amounts of heat) a fusion reactor would have a very high temperature but little actual heat—at least in the area where the fusing is taking place. The energy from the reaction is not transformed into heat until the neutrons are intercepted. As for the stored heat, well, what happens to the stored heat in an oil-fired boiler when the fire goes out? The amounts of heat are comparable; an 8000 megaWatt generator doesn't care if the calories come from burning coal, nuclear fusion, or buffalo chips, it wants the same amount of heat to generate the same amount of current. Thus if the fusion reaction stops there's no real difference from the case when a coal or oil burner stops: the cooling pipes carry away the heat.

But what of a "loss of coolant" accident of the sort that worries opponents of fission plants? There the fusion system is in excellent shape. A fission plant has in addition to the fissionables themselves a vast quantity of moderating substance, and this gets just as hot as the fuel elements; it takes time to remove all this heat, and if there's no cooling the temperatures could go up to a point at which the fuel containers melt even though the nuclear reaction has been shut down. Fusion, though, takes place in a comparatively cool-walled reactor, the plasma itself furnishing the heat; the plasma cools quickly; and the whole system shuts down with quite predictable effects.

A commercial-size fusion reactor will almost

certainly be confined in a steel-and-concrete containment similar to those around fission plants, just to make certain that any problems inside *stay* inside. I suppose someone is working on preliminary designs for a complete reactor now. Unfortunately there's no serious effort at that, because we don't have a national commitment to a working fusion reactor; and we really ought to start such work now so that it can all phase together. It would be a real pity if the scientific teams with their really difficult problems got far ahead of the engineers/safety experts/political analysists/public relations types who have to see that the complete system is both safe and *believably safe*.

But that would imply that the government *wants* cheap fusion systems, and I am not at all sure they do. After all, we're talking revolution, and government workers don't like revolutionaries like you and me.

*　*　*

Another item awaiting my return was an article in SCIENCE NEWS about Robert Bussard's latest conceptual breakthrough. Bussard will be familiar to old-time SF fans as the inventor of the "Bussard Ramjet," a system for using interstellar hydrogen to fuel slower-than-light starships; Poul Anderson used the concept in *Tau Zero* and Larry Niven has incorporated Bussard Ramjets in many of his stories.

Bussard thinks he could have a working fusion reactor by 1985, and build it for vastly smaller sums than are going into the Princeton Tokamak. His machine looks a bit like a Tokamak, and is a magnetic-confinement system; but it is a very great deal smaller, and isn't designed to last very long. The SCIENCE NEWS article called them "throwaway reactors" and that's very nearly right: instead of superconducting magnets as used by Princeton, Bussard would use special alloys of copper.

Because the copper needn't be kept at super-cold temperatures, it could be closer to the reaction. Thus the reactor would be smaller, and a *lot* cheaper.

The neutrons would destroy the copper, trans-muting part of it into cobalt and nickel; Bussard estimates that his reactors would work for only 30 to 40 days before they would have to go off-line for refurbishing; but they are vastly cheaper than the supercold superconducting reactors, so that a utility could operate a number of them in mod-ular-unit fashion. As one fails another comes on line to continue power generation.

Bussard is no bluesky dreamer. He's a former manager of the laser fusion program at Los Alamos and former associate director of magnetic con-finement fusion for the old AEC. He has a docto-rate in plasma physics (Princeton) and two en-gineering degrees, and he was the major force be-hind the first nuclear rocket program.

But no one wants to try his scheme. The De-partment of Energy has turned him down every time. The last time, according to Bussard, the DOE rejection paper contained 11 technical or factual errors. According to SCIENCE NEWS "several con-gressional observers and technicians in the Office of Management and Budget feel that DOE has as-sumed a very political and adversarial role toward the project, unrelated to any possible merits of the proposal."

And get this: Bussard's initial request is under $10 million—chickenfeed. HEW spends that between lunch and teatime every day. (To be precise HEW spends 10 million dollars every 80 minutes, day and night 365 days a year.) So why is DOE "lobbying aggressively" against Bussard's proposal?

Because it might work?

* * *

Cheap energy would bring on a revolution. Make no mistake about that. The history of freedom has largely been the history of what mankind could afford: the higher the technology the larger the pie; the larger the pie, the larger the slice even for the worst off. In the wealthy West there are few who work for a "living"; you need not work much in order not to starve. The poorest among us have what Aristotle thought of as the very criterion of aristocracy: enough leisure time to allow study and participation in public affairs.

Cheap and plentiful energy would do far more than that. It would end forever the whole concept of a "lower class;" and by so doing greatly reduce the power and privileges of the bureaucrats and the new power elites—those who are convinced that what's wrong with the world is all those people out there doing things without permission.

We could see, in our lifetimes, a world in which there are real freedoms, real choices, for everyone on this earth; a world in which no one, simply in order to live, can be forced to submit to indignities.

And that would be a revolution indeed. No wonder, comrades, there are those who don't want to see it.   ●

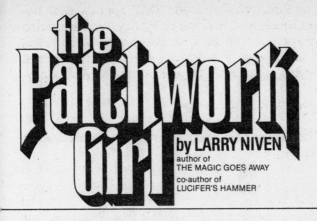

the Patchwork Girl

by LARRY NIVEN

author of
THE MAGIC GOES AWAY

co-author of
LUCIFER'S HAMMER

Naomi Mitchison, the most beautiful woman
on the moon, is charged with murder and must repay society
with bits and pieces of her body (an "eye for an eye").
But investigator Gil Hamilton knows she is innocent
and is working very fast to keep her
from becoming "The Patchwork Girl".

LARRY

NIVEN

Special Trade Publication

Magnificently
Illustrated

$5.95

ACE
SCIENCE
FICTION

Available wherever paperbacks are sold, or order by mail from Book Mailing Service, Ace Science Fiction Division, Box 690, Rockville Centre, N.Y. 11571. Please add 50¢ postage and handling.

ASSIMILATING OUR CULTURE, THAT'S WHAT THEY'RE DOING

BY LARRY NIVEN

Is it
soup yet?

I was putting glasses in the dishwasher when some chirps walked in with three glig in tow. You didn't see many glig in the Draco Tavern. They were grey and compact beings, proportioned like a human linebacker, much shorter than the chirpsithtra. They wore furs against Earth's cold, fur patterned in three tones of green, quite pretty.

It was the first time I'd seen the Silent Stranger react to anything.

He was sitting alone at the bar, as usual. He was forty or so, burly and fit, with thick black hair on his head and his arms. He'd been coming in once or twice a week for at least a year. He never talked to anyone, except me, and then only to order; he'd drink alone, and leave at the end of the night in a precarious rolling walk. Normal enough for the average bar, but not for the Draco.

I have to keep facilities for a score of aliens. Liquors for humans, sparkers for chirps, flavored absolute alcohol for thtopar, spongecake soaked in cyanide solution — and I keep a damn close watch on that — lumps of what I've been calling green kryptonite, and there's never been a roseyfin in here to call for it. My customers don't tend to be loud, but the sound of half a dozen species in conversation is beyond imagination, doubled or tripled because they're all using translating widgets. I need some pretty esoteric sound-proofing.

All of which makes the Draco expensive to run. I charge twenty bucks a drink, ten for sparkers, and so forth. Why would anyone come in here to drink in privacy? I'd wondered about the Silent Stranger.

Then three glig came in, and the Silent Stranger turned his chair away from the bar, but not before I saw his face.

Gail was already on her way to the big table where the glig and the chirps were taking seats, so that was okay. I left the dishwasher half filled. I leaned across the bar and spoke close to the Silent Stranger's ear.

"It's almost surprising how few fights we get in here."

He didn't seem to know I was there.

I said, "I've only seen six in thirty-two years. Even then, nobody got badly hurt. Except once. Some nut, human, tried to shoot a chirp, and a thtopar had to crack his skull. Of course the thtopar didn't know how hard to hit him. I sometimes wish I'd gotten there faster."

He turned just enough to look me in the eye. I said, "I saw your face. I don't know what you've got against the glig, but if you think you're ready to kill them, I think I'm ready to stop you. Have a drink on the house instead."

He said, "The correct name is gligstith(click) optok."

"That's pretty good. I never get the click right."

"It should be good. I was on the first embassy ship to Gligstith(click)tcharf." Bitterly, "There won't be any fight. I can't even punch a glig in the face without making the evening news. It'd all come out."

Gail came back with orders: sparkers for the

chirps and the gligs wanted bull shots, consommé and vodka, with no ice and no flavorings. They were sitting in the high chairs that bring a human face to the level of a chirp's, and their strange hands were waving wildly. I filled the orders with half an eye on the Stranger, who watched me with a brooding look, and I got back to him as soon as I could.

He asked, "Ever wonder why there wasn't any second embassy to Gligstith(click)tcharf?"

"Not especially."

"Why not?"

I shrugged. For two million years there wasn't anything in the universe but us and the gods. Then came the chirps. Then *bang*, a dozen others, and news of thousands more. We're learning so much from the chirps themselves, and of course there's culture shock.

He said, "You know what we brought back. The gligs sold us some advanced medical and agricultural techniques, including templates for the equipment. The chirps couldn't have done that for us. They aren't DNA-based. Why didn't we go back for more?"

"You tell me."

He seemed to brace himself. "I will, then. You serve them in here, you should know about them. Build yourself a drink, on me."

I built two scotch-and-sodas. I asked, "Did you say *sold?* What did we pay them? That didn't make the news."

"It better not. Hell, where do I start? ... The first thing they did when we landed, they gave us a full medical checkup. Very professional. Blood samples, throat scrapings, little nicks in our ears, deep-radar for our innards. We didn't object. Why should we? The gligs are DNA-based. We could have been carrying bacteria that could live off them.

"Then we did the tourist bit. I was having the time of my life! I'd never been further than the Moon. To be in an alien star system, exploring their cities, oh, man! We were all having a ball. We made speeches. We asked about other races. The chirps may claim to own the galaxy, but they don't know everything. There are places they can't go except in special suits, because they grew up around red dwarf stars."

"I know."

"The glig sun is hotter than Sol. We did most of our traveling at night. We went through museums, with cameras following us. Public conferences. We recorded the one on art forms; maybe you saw it."

"Yeah."

"Months of that. Then they wanted us to record a permission for reproduction rights. For that they would pay us a royalty, and sell us certain things on credit against the royalties." He gulped hard at his drink. "You've seen all of that. The medical deep-radar that does what an X-ray does without giving you cancer, and the cloning techniques to grow organ transplants, and the cornucopia plant, and all the rest. And of course we were all for giving them their permission right away.

"Except, do you remember Bill Hersey? He was a reporter and a novelist before he joined the expedition. He wanted details. Exactly what rights did the glig want? Would they be selling permissions

to other species? Were there groups like libraries
or institutes for the blind that got them free? And
they told us. They didn't have anything to hide."

His eyes went to the glig, and mine followed his.
They looked ready for another round. The most
human thing about the glig was their hands, and
their hands were disconcerting. Their palms were
very short and their fingers were long, with an
extra joint. As if a torturer had cut a human palm
between the finger bones, almost to the wrist.
Those hands grabbed the attention . . . but tonight
I could see nothing but the wide mouths and the
shark's array of teeth. Maybe I'd already guessed.

"Clones," said the Silent Stranger. "They took
clones from our tissue samples. The glig grow

clones from almost a hundred DNA-based life forms. They wanted us for their dinner tables, not to mention their classes in exobiology. You know, they couldn't see why we were so upset."

"I don't see why you signed."

"Well, they weren't growing actual human beings. They wanted to grow livers and muscle tissue and marrow without the bones . . . you know, meat. Even a f-f-f — " He had the shakes. A long pull at his scotch and soda stopped that, and he said, "Even a full suckling roast would be grown headless. But the bottom line was that if we didn't give our permissions, there would be pirate editions, and we wouldn't get any royalties. Anyway, we signed. Bill Hersey hanged himself after we came home."

I couldn't think of anything to say, so I built us two more drinks, strong, on the house. Looking back on it, that was my best answer anyway. We touched glasses and drank deep, and he said, "It's a whole new slant on the War of the Worlds. The man-eating monsters are civilized, they're cordial, they're perfect hosts. Nobody gets slaughtered, and think what they're saving on transportation costs! And ten thousand glig carved me up for dinner tonight. The UN made about half a cent per."

Gail was back. Aliens don't upset her, but she was badly upset. She kept her voice down. "The glig would like to try other kinds of meat broth. I don't know if they're kidding or not. They said they wanted — they wanted — "

"They'll take Campbell's," I told her, "and like it." ●

Skystalk

by Charles Sheffield

The more powerful
a technology,
the greater
the fruits thereof—
and the danger...

Illustrated by Steve Fabian

Finlay's Law: Trouble comes at three a.m.

That's always been my experience, and I've learned to dread the hand on my shoulder that shakes me to wakefulness. My dreams had been bad enough, blasting off into orbit on top of an old chemical rocket, riding the torch, up there on a couple of thousand tons of volatile explosives. I'll never understand the nerve of the old-timers, willing to sit up there on one of those monsters.

I shuddered, forced my eyes open, and looked up at Marston's anxious face. I was already sitting up.

"Trouble?" It was a stupid question, but you're allowed a couple of those when you first wake up.

His voice was shaky. "There's a bomb on the Beanstalk."

I was off the bunk, pulling on my undershirt and groping around for my shoes. Larry Marston's words pulled me bolt upright.

"What do you mean, *on* the Beanstalk?"

"That's what Velasquez told me. He won't say more until you get on the line. They're holding a coded circuit open to Earth."

I gave up my search for shoes and went barefoot after Marston. If Arnold Velasquez were right—and I didn't see how he could be—then one of my old horrors was coming true. The Beanstalk had been designed to withstand most natural events, but sabotage was one thing that could never be fully ruled out. At any moment, we had nearly four hundred buckets climbing the Stalk and the same number going down. With the best screening in the world, with hefty rewards for information even of *rumors* of sabotage, there was always the small chance that something could be sneaked through on an outbound bucket. I had less worries about the buckets that went down to Earth. Sabotage from the space end had little to offer its perpetrators, and the Colonies would provide an unpleasant form of death to anyone who tried it, with no questions asked.

Arnold Velasquez was sitting in front of his screen door at Tether Control in Quito. Next to him stood a man I recognized only from news pictures: Otto Panosky, a top aide to the President. Neither man seemed to be looking at the screen. I wondered what they were seeing on their inward eye.

"Jack Finlay here," I said. "What's the story, Arnold?"

There was a perceptible lag before his head came up to stare at the screen, the quarter of a second that it took the video signal to go down to Earth, then back up to synchronous orbit.

"It's best if I read it to you, Jack," he said. At least his voice was under control, even though I could see his hands shaking as they held the paper. "The President's Office got this in over the telecopier about twenty minutes ago."

He rubbed at the side of his face, in the nervous gesture that I had seen during most major stages of the Beanstalk's construction. "It's addressed to us, here in Sky Stalk Control. It's quite short. 'To the Head of Space Transportation Systems. A fusion bomb has been placed in one of the out-going buckets. It is of four megaton capacity, and was armed prior to placement. The secondary activation command can be given at any time by a coded radio signal. Unless terms are met by the President and World Congress on or before 02.00 U.T., seventy-two hours from now, we will give the command to explode the device. Our terms are set out in the following four paragraphs. One—' "

"Never mind those, Arnold." I waved my hand, impatient at the signal delay. "Just tell me one thing. Will Congress meet their demands?"

He shook his head. "They can't. What's being asked for is preposterous in the time available. You know how much red tape there is in inter-governmental relationships."

"You told them that?"

"Of course. We sent out a general broadcast." He shrugged. "It was no good. We're dealing with fa-natics, with madmen. I need to know what you can do at your end."

"How much time do we have now?"

He looked at his watch. "Seventy-one and a half hours, if they mean what they say. You understand that we have no idea which bucket might be carry-ing the bomb. It could have been planted there days ago, and still be on the way up."

He was right. The buckets—there were three hundred and eighty-four of them each way—moved at a steady five kilometers a minute, up or down. That's a respectable speed, but it still took almost five days for each one of them to climb the cable of the Beanstalk out to our position in syn-chronous orbit.

Then I thought a bit more, and decided he wasn't quite right.

"It's not that vague, Arnold. You can bet the bomb wasn't placed on a bucket that started out more than two days ago. Otherwise, we could wait for it to get here and disarm it, and still be inside their deadline. It must still be fairly close to Earth, I'd guess."

"Well, even if you're right, that deduction doesn't help us." He was chewing a pen to bits between sentences. "We don't have anything here that could be ready in time to fly out and take a look, even if it's only a couple of thousand kilometers. Even if we did, and even if we could spot the bomb, we couldn't rendezvous with a bucket on the Stalk. That's why I need to know what you can do from your end. Can you handle it from there?"

I took a deep breath and swung my chair to face Larry Marston.

"Larry, four megatons would vaporize a few kilometers of the main cable. How hard would it be for us to release ballast at the top end of the cable, above us here, enough to leave this station in position?"

"Well . . ." He hesitated. "We could do that, Jack. But then we'd lose the power satellite. It's right out at the end there, by the ballast. Without it, we'd lose all the power at the station here, and all the buckets too—there isn't enough reserve power to keep the magnetic fields going. We'd need all our spare power to keep the recycling going here."

That was the moment when I finally came fully awake. I realized the implications of what he was saying, and was nodding before he'd finished speaking. Without adequate power, we'd be looking at a very messy situation.

"And it wouldn't only be us," I said to Velasquez and Panosky, sitting there tense in front of their screen. "Everybody on the Colonies will run low on air and water if the supply through the Stalk breaks down. Dammit, we've been warning Congress how vulnerable we are for years. All the time, there've been fewer and fewer rocket launches, and nothing but foot-dragging on getting the second Stalk started with a Kenya tether. Now you want miracles from us at short notice."

If I sounded bitter, that's because I *was* bitter. Panosky was nodding his head in a conciliatory way.

"We know, Jack. And if you can pull us through this one, I think you'll see changes in the future. But right now, we can't debate that. We have to know what you can do for us *now*, this minute."

I couldn't argue with that. I swung my chair again to face Larry Marston.

"Get Hasse and Kano over here to the Control Room as soon as you can." I turned back to Velasquez. "Give us a few minutes here, while we get organized. I'm bringing in the rest of my top engineering staff."

While Larry was rounding up the others, I sat back and let the full dimensions of the problem sink in. Sure, if we had to we could release the ballast at the outward end of the Stalk. If the Beanstalk below us were severed we'd have to do that, or be whipped out past the Moon like a stone from a slingshot, as the tension in the cable suddenly dropped.

But if we did that, what would happen to the piece of the Beanstalk that was still tethered to Earth, anchored down there in Quito? There might be as much as thirty thousand kilometers of it, and as soon as the break occurred it would begin to fall.

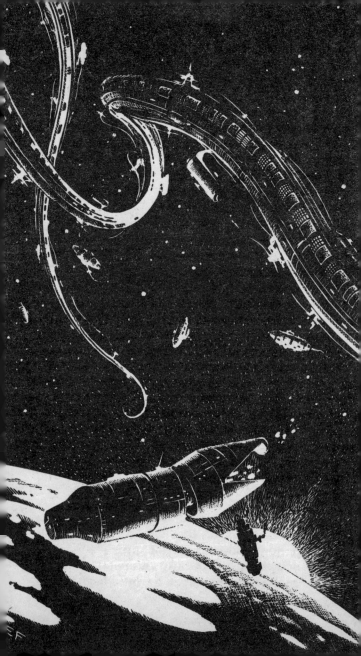

Not in a straight line. That wasn't the way that the dynamics went. It would begin to curl around the Earth, accelerating as it went, cracking into the atmosphere along the equator like a billion-ton whip stretching half-way around the planet. Forget the carrier buckets, and the superconducting cables that carried electricity down to the drive train from the solar power satellite seventy thousand kilometers above us. The piece that would do the real damage would be the central, load-bearing cable itself. It was only a couple of meters across at the bottom end, but it widened steadily as it went up. Made of bonded and doped silicon whiskers, with a tensile strength of two hundred million Newtons per square centimeter, it could handle an incredible load—almost two-thirds of a billion tons at its thinnest point. When that stored energy hit the atmosphere, there was going to be a fair amount of excitement down there on the surface. Not that we'd be watching it—the loss of the power satellite would make us look at our own survival problems; and as for the Colonies, a century of development would be ended.

By the time that Larry Marston came back with Jen Hasse and Alicia Kano, I doubt if I looked any more cheerful than Arnold Velasquez, down there at Tether Control. I sketched out the problem to the two newcomers; we had what looked like a hopeless situation on our hands.

"We have seventy-one hours," I concluded. "The only question we need to answer is, what will we be doing at this end during that time? Tether Control can coordinate disaster planning for the position on Earth. Arnold has already ruled out the possibility of any actual *help* from Earth—there are no rockets there that could be ready in time."

"What about the repair robots that you have on the cable?" asked Panosky, jumping into the conversation. "I thought they were all the way along its length."

"They are," said Jen Hasse. "But they're special purpose, not general purpose. We couldn't use one to look for a radioactive signal on a bucket, if that's what you're thinking of. Even if they had the right sensors for it, we'd need a week to reprogram them for the job."

"We don't have a week," said Alicia quietly. "We have seventy-one hours." She was small and dark-haired, and never raised her voice much above the minimum level needed to reach her audience—but I had grown to rely on her brains more than anything else on the station.

"Seventy-one hours, if we act *now*," I said. "We've already agreed that we don't have time to sit here and wait for that bucket with the bomb to arrive— the terrorists must have planned it that way."

"I know." Alicia did not raise her voice. "Sitting and waiting won't do it. But the total travel time of a carrier from the surface up to synchronous orbit, or back down again, is a little less than a hundred and twenty hours. That means that the bucket carrying the bomb will be at least *half-way* here in sixty hours. And a bucket that started down from here in the next few hours—"

"—would have to pass the bucket with the bomb on the way up, before the deadline," broke in Hasse. He was already over at the Control Board, looking at the carrier schedule. He shook his head. "There's nothing scheduled for a passenger bucket, in the next twenty-four hours. It's all cargo going down."

"We're not looking for luxury." I went across to look at the schedule. "There are a couple of ore buckets with heavy metals scheduled for the next three hours. They'll have plenty of space in the top of them, and they're just forty minutes apart from each other. We could squeeze somebody in one or both of them, provided they were properly suited up. It wouldn't be a picnic, sitting in suits for three days, but we could do it."

"So how would we get at the bomb, even if we did that?" asked Larry. "It would be on the other side of the Beanstalk from us, passing at a relative velocity of six hundred kilometers an hour. We couldn't do more than wave to it as it went by, even if we knew just which bucket was carrying the bomb."

"That's the tricky piece." I looked at Jen Hasse. 'Do you have enough control over the mass driver system, to slow everything almost to a halt whenever an inbound and an outbound bucket pass each other?"

He was looking doubtful, rubbing his nose thoughtfully. "Maybe. Trouble is, I'd have to do it nearly a hundred times, if you want to slow down for every pass. And it would take me twenty minutes to stop and start each one. I don't think we have that much time. What do you have in mind?"

I went across to the model of the Beanstalk that we kept on the Control Room table. We often found that we could illustrate things with it in a minute that would have taken thousands of words to describe.

"Suppose we were here, starting down in a bucket," I said. I put my hand on the model of the station, thirty-five thousand kilometers above the surface of the Earth in synchronous orbit. "And

suppose that the bucket we want to get to, the one
with the bomb, is here, on the way up. We put
somebody in the inbound bucket, and it starts on
down."

I began to turn the drive train, so that the buckets
began to move up and down along the length of the
Beanstalk.

"The people in the inbound bucket carry a radiation counter," I went on. "We'd have to put it on a
long arm, so that it cleared all the other stuff on the
Stalk, and reached around to get near the upbound
buckets. We can do that, I'm sure—if we can't, we
don't deserve to call ourselves engineers. We stop
at each outbound carrier, and test for radioactivity.
There should be enough of that from the fission
trigger of the bomb, so that we'll easily pick up a
count when we reach the right bucket. Then you,
Jan, hold the drive train in the halt position. We

leave the inbound bucket, swing around the Stalk, and get into the other carrier. Then we try and disarm the bomb. I've had some experience with that."

"You mean we get out and actually *climb* around the Beanstalk?" asked Larry. He didn't sound pleased at the prospect.

"Right. It shouldn't be too bad," I said. "We can anchor ourselves with lines to the ore bucket, so we can't fall."

Even as I was speaking, I realized that it didn't sound too plausible. Climbing around the outside of the Beanstalk in a space-suit, twenty thousand kilometers or more up, dangling on a line connected to an ore bucket—and then trying to take apart a fusion bomb wearing gloves. No wonder Larry didn't like the sound of that assignment. I wasn't surprised when Arnold Velasquez chipped in over the circuit connecting us to Tether Control.

"Sorry, Jack, but that won't work—even if you could do it. You didn't let me read the full message from the terrorists. One of their conditions is that we mustn't stop the bucket train on the Stalk in the next three days. I think they were afraid that we would reverse the direction of the buckets, and bring the bomb back down to Earth to disarm it. I guess they don't realize that the Stalk wasn't designed to run in reverse."

"Damnation. What else do they have in that message?" I asked. "What can they do if we decide to stop the bucket drive anyway? How can they even tell that we're doing it?"

"We have to assume that they have a plant in here at Tether Control," replied Velasquez. "After all, they managed to get a bomb onto the Stalk in spite of all our security. They say they'll explode the bomb if we make any attempt to slow or stop the bucket train, and we simply can't afford to take the risk of doing that. We have to assume they can monitor what's going on with the Stalk drive train."

There was a long, dismal silence, which Alicia finally broke.

"So that seems to leave us with only one alternative," she said thoughtfully. Then she grimaced and pouted her mouth. "It's a two-bucket operation, and I don't even like to think about it—even though I had a grandmother who was a circus trapeze artiste."

She was leading in to something, and it wasn't like her to make a big build-up.

"That bad, eh?" I said.

"That bad, if we're lucky," she said. "If we're unlucky, I guess we'd all be dead in a month or two anyway, as the recycling runs down. For this to work, we need a good way of dissipating a lot of kinetic energy—something like a damped mechanical spring would do it. And we need a good way of sticking to the side of the Beanstalk. Then, we use *two* ore buckets—forty minutes apart would be all right—like this . . ."

She went over to the model of the Beanstalk. We watched her with mounting uneasiness as she outlined her idea. It sounded crazy. The only trouble was, it was that or nothing. Making choices in those circumstances is not difficult.

One good thing about space maintenance work—you develop versatility. If you can't wait to locate something down on Earth, then waste another week or so to have it shipped up to you,

you get into the habit of making it for yourself. In an hour or so, we had a sensitive detector ready, welded on to a long extensible arm on the side of a bucket. When it was deployed, it would reach clear around the Beanstalk, missing all the drive train and repair station fittings, and hang in close to the outbound buckets. Jen had fitted it with a gadget that moved the detector rapidly upwards at the moment of closest approach of an upbound carrier, to increase the length of time available for getting a measurement of radioactivity. He swore that it would work on the fly, and have a better than ninety-nine percent chance of telling us which outbound bucket contained the bomb—even with a relative fly-by speed of six hundred kilometers an hour.

I didn't have time to argue the point, and in any case Jen was the expert. I also couldn't dispute his

claim that he was easily the best qualified person to operate the gadget. He and Larry Marston, both fully suited-up, climbed into the ore bucket. We had to leave the ore in there, because the mass balance between in-going and outbound buckets was closely calculated to give good stability to the Beanstalk. It made for a lumpy seat, but no one complained. Alicia and I watched as the bucket was moved into the feeder system, accelerated up to the correct speed, attached to the drive train, and dropped rapidly out of sight down the side of the Beanstalk.

"That's the easy part," she said. "They drop with the bucket, checking the upbound ones as they come by for radioactivity, and that's all they have to do."

"Unless they can't detect any signal," I said. "Then the bomb goes off, and they have the world's biggest roller-coaster ride. Twenty thousand kilometers of it, with the big thrill at the end."

"They'd never reach the surface," replied Alicia absent-mindedly. "They'll frizzle up in the atmosphere long before they get there. Or maybe they won't. I wonder what the terminal velocity would be if you hung onto the Stalk cable?"

As she spoke, she was calmly examining an odd device that had been produced with impossible haste in the machine shop on the station's outer rim. It looked like an old-fashioned parachute harness, but instead of the main chute the lines led to a wheel about a meter across. From the opposite edge of the wheel, a doped silicon rope led to a hefty magnetic grapnel. Another similar arrangement was by her side.

"Here," she said to me. "Get yours on over your

suit, and let's make sure we both know how to handle them. If you miss with the grapple, it'll be messy."

I looked at my watch. "We don't have time for any dry run. In the next fifteen minutes we have to get our suits on, over to the ore buckets, and into these harnesses. Anyway, I don't think rehearsals here inside the station mean too much when we get to the real thing."

We looked at each other for a moment, then began to suit up. It's not easy to estimate odds for something that has never been done before, but I didn't give us more than one chance in a hundred of coming out of it safely. Suits and harnesses on, we went and sat without speaking in the ore bucket.

I saw that we were sitting on a high-value shipment—silver and platinum, from one of the

Belt mining operations. It wasn't comfortable, but we were certainly traveling in expensive company. Was it King Midas who complained that a golden throne is not right for restful sitting?

No matter what the final outcome, we were in for an unpleasant trip. Our suits had barely enough capacity for a six-day journey. They had no recycling capacity, and if we had to go all the way to the halfway point we would be descending for almost sixty hours. We had used up three hours to the deadline, getting ready to go, so that would leave us only nine hours to do something about the bomb when we reached it. I suppose that it was just as bad or worse for Hasse and Marston. After they'd done their bit with the detector, there wasn't a thing they could do except sit in their bucket and wait, either for a message from us or an explosion far above them.

"Everything all right down there, Larry?" I asked, testing the radio link with them for the umpteenth time.

"Can't tell." He sounded strained. "We've passed three buckets so far, outbound ones, and we've had no signal from the detector. I guess that's as planned, but it would be nice to know it's working all right."

"You shouldn't expect anything for at least thirty-six hours," said Alicia.

"I know that. But it's impossible for us *not* to look at the detector whenever we pass an outbound bucket. Logically, we should be sleeping now and saving our attention for the most likely time of encounter—but neither one of us seems able to do it."

"Don't assume that the terrorists are all that logical, either," I said. "Remember, we are the ones who decided that they must have started the bomb on its way only a few hours ago. It's possible they put it into a bucket three or four days ago, and made up the deadline for some other reason. We think we can disarm that bomb, but they may not agree —and they may be right. All we may manage to do is advance the time of the explosion when we try and open up the casing."

As I spoke, I felt our bucket begin to accelerate. We were heading along the feeder and approaching the bucket drive train. After a few seconds, we were outside the station, dropping down the Beanstalk after Jen and Larry.

We sat there in silence for a while. I'd been up and down the Stalk many times, and so had Alicia, but always in passenger modules. The psychologists had decided that people rode those a lot better when they were windowless. The cargo bucket had no windows either, but we had left the hatch open, to simplify communications with the other bucket and to enable us to climb out if and when the time came. We would have to close it when we were outside, or the aerodynamic pressures would spoil bucket stability when it finally entered the atmosphere—three hundred kilometers an hour isn't that fast, but it's a respectable speed for travel at full atmospheric pressure.

Our bucket was about four meters wide and three deep. It carried a load of seven hundred tons, so our extra mass was negligible. I stood at its edge and looked up, then down. The psychologists were quite right. Windows were a bad idea.

Above us, the Beanstalk rose up and up, occulting the backdrop of stars. It went past the synchronous station, which was still clearly visible as a blob on the stalk, then went on further up, invisible, to the solar power satellite and the great ballast weight, a hundred and five thousand kilometers above the surface of the Earth. On the Stalk itself, I could see the shielded superconductors that ran its full length, from the power satellite down to Tether Control in Quito. We were falling steadily, our rate precisely controlled by the linear synchronous motors that set the accelerations through pulsed magnetic fields. The power for that was drawn from the same superconducting cables. In the event of an electrical power failure, the buckets were designed to 'freeze' to the side of the Stalk with mechanical coupling. We had to build the system that way, because about once a year we had some kind of power interruption—usually from small meteorites, not big enough to trigger the main detector system, but large enough to penetrate the shields and mess up the power transmission.

It was looking down, though, that produced the real effect. I felt my heart begin to pump harder, and I was gripping at the side of the bucket with my space-suit gloves. When you are in a rocket-propelled ship, you don't get any real feeling of height. Earth is another part of the Universe, something independent of you. But from our position, moving along the side of the Beanstalk, I had quite a different feeling. We were *connected* to the planet. I could see the Stalk, dwindling smaller and smaller down to the Earth below. I had a very clear feeling that I could fall all the way down it, down to the big, blue-white globe at its foot. Although I had lived up at the station quite happily for over five years, I

suddenly began to worry about the strength of the main cable. It was a ridiculous concern. There was a safety factor of ten built into its design, far more than a rational engineer would use for anything. It was more likely that the bottom would fall out of our ore bucket, than that the support cable for the Beanstalk would break. I was kicking myself for my illogical fears, until I noticed Alicia also peering out at the Beanstalk, as though trying to see past the clutter of equipment there to the cable itself. I wasn't the only one thinking wild thoughts.

"You certainly get a different look at things from here," I said, trying to change the mood. "Did you ever see anything like that before?"

She shook her head ponderously—the suits weren't made for agility of movement.

"Not up here, I haven't," she replied. "But I once went up to the top of the towers of the Golden Gate Bridge in San Francisco, and looked at the support cables for that. It was the same sort of feeling. I began to wonder if they could take the strain. That was just for a bridge, not even a big one. What will happen if we don't make it, and they blow up the Beanstalk?"

I shrugged, inside my suit, then realized that she couldn't see the movement. "This is the only bridge to space that we've got. We'll be out of the bridge business, and back in the ferry-boat business. They'll have to start sending stuff up by rockets again. Shipments won't be a thousandth of what they are now, until another Stalk can be built. That will take thirty years, starting without this one to help us—even if the Colonies survive all right, and work on nothing else. We don't have to worry about that, though. We won't be there to hassle with it."

She nodded. "We were in such a hurry to get away it never occurred to me that we'd be sitting here for a couple of days with nothing to do but worry. Any ideas?"

"Yes. While you were making the reel and grapnel, I thought about that. The only thing that's worth our attention right now is a better understanding of the geometry of the Stalk. We need to know exactly where to position ourselves, where we'll set the grapnels, and what our dynamics will be as we move. I've asked Ricardo to send us schematics and lay-outs over the suit videos. He's picking out ones that show the drive train, the placing of the superconductors, and the unmanned repair stations. I've also asked him to de-activate all the repair robots. It's better for us to risk a failure on the maintenance side than have one of the monitoring robots wandering along the Stalk and mixing in with what we're trying to do."

"I heard what you said to Panosky, but it still seems to me that the robots ought to be useful."

"I'd hoped so, too. I checked again with Jen, and he agrees we'd have to reprogram them, and we don't have the time for it. It would take weeks. Jen said having them around would be like taking along a half-trained dog, bumbling about while we work. Forget that one."

As we talked, we kept our eyes open for the outbound buckets, passing us on the other side of the Beanstalk. We were only about ten meters from them at closest approach and they seemed to hurtle past us at an impossible speed. The idea of hitching on to one of them began to seem more and more preposterous. We settled down to look in more detail at the configuration of cables, drive

Skystalk   185

train, repair stations and buckets that was being flashed to us over the suit videos.

It was a weary time, an awful combination of boredom and tension. The video images were good, but there is a limit to what you can learn from diagrams and simulations. About once an hour, Jen Hasse and Larry Marston called in from the lower bucket beneath us, reporting on the news—or lack of it—regarding the bomb detection efforts. A message relayed from Panosky at Tether Control reported no progress in negotiations with the terrorists. The fanatics simply didn't believe their terms couldn't be met. That was proof of their naivety, but didn't make them any less dangerous.

It was impossible to get comfortable in our suits. The ore buckets had never been designed for a human occupant, and we couldn't find a level spot to stretch out. Alicia and I passed into a half-awake trance, still watching the images that flashed onto the suit videos, but not taking in much of anything. Given that we couldn't sleep, we were probably in the closest thing we could get to a resting state. I hoped that Jen and Larry would keep their attention up, watching an endless succession of buckets flash past them and checking each one for radioactivity count.

The break came after fifty-four hours in the bucket. We didn't need to hear the details from the carrier below us to know they had it—Larry's voice crackled with excitement.

"Got it," he said. "Jen picked up a strong signal from the bucket we just passed. If you leave the ore carrier within thirty-four seconds, you'll have thirty-eight minutes to get ready for it to come past you. It will be the second one to reach you. For

God's sake don't try for the wrong one."

There was a pause, then Larry said something I would never have expected from him. "We'll lose radio contact with you in a while, as we move further along the Stalk. Good luck, both of you—and look after him, Alicia."

I didn't have time to think that one through—but shouldn't he be telling *me* to look after *her?* It was no time for puzzling. We were up on top of our bucket in a second, adrenalin moving through our veins like an electric current. The cable was whipping past us at a great rate; the idea of forsaking the relative safety of the ore bucket for the naked wall of the Beanstalk seemed like insanity. We watched as one of the repair stations, sticking out from the cable into open space, flashed past.

"There'll be another one of those coming by in

thirty-five seconds," I said. "We've got to get the grapnels onto it, and we'll be casting blind. I'll throw first, and you follow a second later. Don't panic if I miss — remember, we only have to get one good hook there."

"Count us down, Jack," said Alicia. She wasn't one to waste words in a tight spot.

I pressed the digital read-out in my suit, and watched the count move from thirty-five down to zero.

"Count-down display on Channel Six," I said, and picked up the rope and grapnel. I looked doubtfully at the wheel that was set in the middle of the thin rope, then even looked suspiciously at the rope itself, wondering if it would take the strain. That shows how the brain works in a crisis — that rope would have held a herd of elephants with no trouble at all.

I cast the grapnel as the count touched to zero, and Alicia threw a fraction later. Both ropes were spliced onto both suits, so it was never clear which grapnel took hold. Our bucket continued to drop rapidly towards Earth, but we were jerked off the top of it and went zipping on downwards fractionally slower as the friction reel in the middle of the rope unwound, slowing our motion.

We came to a halt about fifty meters down the Beanstalk from the grapnel, after a rough ride in which our deceleration must have averaged over seven gee. Without that reel to slow us down gradually, the jerk of the grapnel as it caught the repair station wall would have snapped our spines when we were lifted from the ore bucket.

We hung there, swinging free, suspended from the wall of the Stalk. As the reel began to take up the line that had been paid out, I made the mistake of looking down. We dangled over an awful void, with nothing between us and that vast drop to the Earth below but the thin line above us. When we came closer to the point of attachment to the Beanstalk wall, I saw just how lucky we had been. One grapnel had missed completely, and the second one had caught the very lip of the repair station platform. Another foot to the left and we would have missed it altogether.

We clawed our way up to the station rim—easy enough to do, because the gravity at that height was only a fraction of a gee, less than a tenth. But a fall from there would be inexorable, and we would have fallen away from the Beanstalk, with no chance to re-connect to it. Working together, we freed the grapnel and readied both lines and grapnels for re-use. After that there was nothing to do but cling to the side of the Beanstalk, watch the sweep of the heavens above us, and wait for the outbound ore buckets to come past us.

The first one came by after seventeen minutes. I had the clock read-out to prove it, otherwise I would have solemnly sworn that we had waited there for more than an hour, holding to our precarious perch. Alicia seemed more at home there than I was. I watched her moving the grapnel to the best position for casting it, then settle down patiently to wait.

It is hard to describe my own feelings in that period. I watched the movement of the stars above us, in their great circle, and wondered if we would be alive in another twenty minutes. I felt a strong communion with the old sailors of Earth's seas, up in their crow's-nest in a howling gale, sensing nothing but darkness, high-blown spindrift, perilous breakers ahead, and the dipping, rolling stars above.

Alicia kept her gaze steadily downwards, something that I found hard to do. She had inherited a good head for heights from her circus-performer grandmother.

"I can see it," she said at last. "All ready for a repeat performance?"

"Right." I swung the grapnel experimentally. "Since we can see it this time, we may as well throw together."

I concentrated on the bucket sweeping steadily up towards us, trying to estimate the distance and the time that it would take before it reached us. We both drew back our arms at the same moment and lobbed the grapnels towards the center of the bucket.

It came past us with a monstrous, silent rush. Again we felt the fierce acceleration as we were jerked away from the Beanstalk wall and shot upwards after the carrier. Again, I realized that we couldn't have done it without Alicia's friction reel, smoothing the motion for us. This time, it was more dangerous than when we had left the downbound bucket. Instead of trying to reach the stationary wall of the Stalk, we were now hooked onto the moving bucket. We swung wildly beneath it in its upward flight, narrowly missing contact with elements of the drive train, and then with another repair station that flashed past a couple of meters to our right.

Finally, somehow, we damped our motion, reeled in the line, slid back the cover to the ore bucket and fell safely forward inside it. I was completely drained. It must have been all nervous stress—we hadn't expended a significant amount of physical energy. I know that Alicia felt the same way as I did, because after we plumped over the rim of the carrier we both fell to the floor and lay there without speaking for several minutes. It gives some idea of our state of mind when I say that the bucket we had reached, with a four megaton bomb inside it that might go off at any moment, seemed like a haven of safety.

We finally found the energy to get up and look around us. The bucket was loaded with manufactured goods, and I thought for a sickening moment that the bomb was not there. We found it after five minutes of frantic searching. It was a compact blue cylinder, a meter long and fifty centimeters wide, and it had been cold-welded to the wall of the bucket. I knew the design.

"There it is," I said to Alicia. Then I didn't know what to say next. It was the most advanced design, not the big, old one that I had been hoping for.

"Can you disarm it?" asked Alicia.

"In principle. There's only one problem. I know how it's put together—but I'll never be able to get it apart wearing a suit. The fingerwork I'd need is just too fine for gloves. We seem to be no better off than we were before."

We sat there side by side, looking at the bomb. The irony of the situation was sinking in. We had reached it, just as we hoped we could. Now, it seemed we might as well have been still back in the station.

"Any chance that we could get it free and dump it overboard?" asked Alicia. "You know, just chuck the thing away from the bucket."

I shook my head, aware again of how much my suit impeded freedom of movement. "It's spot-welded. We couldn't shift it. Anyway, free fall from here would give it an impact orbit, and a lot of people might be killed if it went off inside the atmosphere. If we were five thousand kilometers higher, perigee would be at a safe height above the surface—but we can't afford to wait for another sixteen hours until the bucket gets up that high. Look, I've got another idea, but it will mean that we'll lose radio contact with the station."

"So what?" said Alicia. Her voice was weary. "There's not a thing they can do to help us anyway."

"They'll go out of their minds with worry down on Earth, if they don't know what's happening here."

"I don't see why we should keep all of it for

ourselves. What's your idea, Jack?"

"All right." I summoned my reserves of energy. "We're in vacuum now, but this bucket would be air-tight if we were to close the top hatch again. I have enough air in my suit to make a breathable atmosphere in this enclosed space, at least for long enough to let me have a go at the bomb. We've got nearly twelve hours to the deadline, and if I can't disarm it in that time I can't do it at all."

Alicia looked at her air reserve indicator and nodded. "I can spare you some air, too, if I open up my suit."

"No. We daren't do that. We have one other big problem—the temperature. It's going to feel really cold in here, once I'm outside my suit. I'll put my heaters on to maximum, and leave the suit open, but I'm still not sure I can get much done before I begin to freeze up. If I begin to lose feeling in my fingers, I'll need your help to get me back inside. So you have to stay in your suit. Once I'm warmed up, I can try again."

She was silent for a few moments, repeating the calculations that I had just done myself.

"You'll only have enough air to try it twice," she said at last. "If you can't do it in one shot, you'll have to let me have a go. You can direct me on what has to be done."

There was no point in hanging around. We sent a brief message to the station, telling them what we were going to do, then closed the hatch and began to bleed air out of my suit and into the interior of the bucket. We used the light from Alicia's suit, which had ample power to last for several days.

When the air pressure inside the bucket was high enough for me to breathe, I peeled out of my suit. It was as cold as charity in that metal box, but I ignored that and crouched down alongside the bomb in my underwear and bare feet.

I had eleven hours at the most. Inside my head, I fancied that I could hear a clock ticking. That must have been only my fancy. Modern bombs have no place for clockwork timers.

By placing my suit directly beneath my hands, I found that I could get enough heat from the thermal units to let me keep on working without a break. The clock inside my head went on ticking, also without a break.

On and on and on.

They say that I was delirious when we reached the station. That's the only way the Press could reconcile my status as public hero with the things that I said to the President when he called up to congratulate us.

I suppose I could claim delirium if I wanted to—five days without sleep, two without food, oxygen starvation, and frostbite of the toes and ears, that might add up to delirium. I had received enough warmth from the suit to keep my hands going, because it was very close to them, but that had been at the expense of some of my other extremities. If it hadn't been for Alicia, cramming me somehow back into the suit after I had disarmed the bomb, I would have frozen to death in a couple of hours.

As it was, I smelled ripe and revolting when they unpacked us from the bucket and winkled me out of my suit—Alicia hadn't been able to re-connect me with the plumbing arrangements.

So I told the President that the World Congress

was composed of a giggling bunch of witless turds, who couldn't sense a global need for more bridges to space if a Beanstalk were pushed up their backsides—which was where I thought they kept their brains. Not quite the speech that we used to get from the old-time returning astronauts, but I must admit it's one that I'd wanted to give for some time. The audience was there this time, with the whole world hanging on my words over live TV.

We've finally started construction on the second Beanstalk. I don't know if my words had anything to do with it, but there was a lot of public pressure after I said my piece, and I like to think that I had some effect.

And me? I'm designing the third Beanstalk; what else? But I don't think I'll hold my breath waiting for a Congressional Vote of Thanks for my efforts saving the first one.

"WHY USE SOMETHING
AS WASTEFUL AND NOISY
AS A ROCKET
WHEN THERE ARE SIMPLE,
CLEAN, EFFICIENT
ALTERNATIVES?"

HOW TO BUILD A BEANSTALK

by Charles Sheffield

Illustrated by David Egge

THE AGE OF ROCKETS.

The launch of a Saturn V rocket is an impressive sight. It is impressively noisy, impressively big and impressively risky. It is also one of Man's outstanding examples of conspicuous consumption, where a few thousand tons of fuel go up (literally) in smoke (literally) in a couple of minutes. And yet it is, in 1979, the best space transportation system that we have.

If we were to sit down and make a list of the

properties of our 'ideal' space transportation system, without worrying about whether or not we could ever hope to achieve it, what would it look like? Well, first and most important it ought not to use up any raw materials in its working—no reaction mass, which all rockets need to propel themselves. It ought to allow us to take materials up and down from planetary surfaces, and be equally good at moving us around in free space. And it would be nice if it were somehow completely energy-free. While we are at it, let's ask that it be also silent and non-polluting.

Note that our old friend, the rocket, satisfies *none* of our ideal system requirements. The Space Shuttle, our first reusable spacecraft, is not suited to anything beyond low earth orbit activities, and is, with all its advantages over its non-reusable predecessors, still a very primitive system.

It may sound improbable, but an ideal space system, satisfying *all* our requirements, could be here in a couple of generations. As we shall see, the technology needed is not far from that already available to us.

It is curious that science fiction, which likes to look beyond today's technology, has remained so infatuated with the idea of rockets. Some people even use them to *define* the field. Look at the 'sf' section in public libraries and you will often see a small drawing of a rocket attached to the spine of each volume. It may be a perverse choice of label for a branch of writing that covers everything from 'Ringworld' to 'Flowers For Algernon', but you can see how the logic goes; science fiction means space travel, and space travel means rockets—because they are 'the only way of getting up to space and around in space.' After all, there is nothing for any other sort of transportation to 'push against' in space. Right?

Not quite. We will try and dispose of that peculiar viewpoint here. Our preoccupation with rockets for space travel will probably amaze our descendants.

"Why use something as wasteful and noisy as a rocket," they will ask, "when there are simple, clean, efficient alternatives? Why didn't they use Beanstalks?"

The Age of Rockets may look to them like the Age of Dinosaurs. Let's try and see it through their eyes, beginning with the most basic principles.

A spacecraft, orbiting Earth around the equator just high enough to avoid the main effects of atmospheric drag, makes a complete revolution in about an hour and a half. If the Earth had no atmosphere, a spacecraft in a 'grazing orbit' would skim around just above the surface in 84.9 minutes. At the end of that time, it would *not* be above the same point on the Earth where it started. The Earth is rotating, too, and if the spacecraft revolves in the same direction as Earth it must go farther—about 2,370 kilometers, the distance that a point on the equator rotates in 84.9 minutes—before it again passes over the point where it began.

Now keep the spacecraft in a circular path above the equator, but instead of a grazing orbit, imagine that it travels 1,000 kilometers above the surface. Then the orbital period will be greater. It will now be about 106 minutes: the higher the orbit, the longer the period of revolution.

When the height of the spacecraft is 35,770 kilometers, the orbital period is 1,436 minutes, or one sidereal day (a *solar* day, the time that a point on the Earth takes to return to point exactly at the Sun, is 1,440 minutes). In other words, the spacecraft now takes just as long as the Earth to make one full revolution in space. Since the spacecraft is moving around at the same rate as the Earth, it seems to hover always above the same point on the equator.

Such a specialized orbit is called *geostationary*, because the satellite does not move relative to the Earth's surface. It is a splendid orbit for a communications satellite. There is no need for ground receiving antennae to track the satellite at all—it remains in one place in the sky. The term 'Clarkian orbit' has been proposed as an alternate to the cumbersome 'geostationary orbit', in recognition of Arthur Clarke's original suggestion in 1945 that such orbits had unique potential for use in worldwide communications. Note, by the way, that a 24-hour period orbit does not have to be geostationary. An orbit whose plane is at an angle to the equator can be *geosynchronous*, with 24-hour period, but it moves up and down in latitude and oscillates in longitude during one day. The class of geosynchronous orbits includes all geostationary orbits.

A geosynchronous orbit has some other unusual features. It is at the distance from the Earth where gravitational and centrifugal accelerations on an orbiting object balance. To see what this means, suppose that you could erect a thin pole vertically on the equator. A long pole, and I do mean *long*. Suppose that you could extend it upwards over a hundred thousand kilometers, and it was strong and rigid enough that you could make it remain vertical. Then every part of the pole *below* the height of a geostationary orbit would feel a net downward force, because it is travelling too slowly for centrifugal acceleration to balance gravitational acceleration. On the other hand, every element of the pole beyond geostationary altitude would feel a net *outward* force. Those elements are travelling so fast that centrifugal force exceeds gravitational pull.

(Every mechanics textbook will point out that there are no such things as 'centrifugal forces'; there is only the gravitational force, curving the path of the orbiting body from its natural inclination to continue in a straight line. The centrifugal forces are fictitious forces, arising only as a consequence of the use of a rotating reference frame for calculations. But centrifugal forces are so convenient that everyone uses them, even if they don't exist! And when you move to an Einsteinian viewpoint you find that centrifugal forces now appear as real as any others. So much for theories.)

The higher that a section of the pole is above geostationary height, the greater the total outward pull on it. So if we make the pole just the right length, the total inward pull from all parts of the pole *below* geostationary height will exactly balance the outward pull from the higher sections *above* that height. Our pole will hang there, touching the Earth at the equator but not exerting any downward force on it. If you like, we can think of the pole as an enormously long satellite, in a geostationary orbit.

How long would such a pole have to be? If we were to make the pole of uniform cross-section, it would have to extend upwards a distance of about

143,700 kilometers. This result does not depend on the cross-sectional area of the pole, nor on the material from which it is made. It should be clear that in practice we would not choose to make a pole of uniform cross-section, since the downward pull that it must withstand is far greater up near geosynchronous height than it is near the Earth. At the higher point, the pole must support the weight of more than 35,000 kilometers of itself, whereas near Earth it supports only the weight hanging below it. From this, we would expect that the best design will be a tapered pole, with its thickest part at geostationary altitude where the pull on it is greatest.

The idea of a rigid pole is also misleading. We have seen that the only forces at work are tensions. It is thus more logical to think of the structure as a *cable* than a pole.

We now have the major feature of our 'basic Beanstalk'. It will be a long, strong cable, extending from the surface of the Earth on the equator, out to beyond the geostationary orbit. It will be of the order of 144,000 kilometers long. We will use it as the load-bearing cable of a giant elevator, to send materials up to orbit and back. The structure will hang there in static equilibrium, revolving with the Earth. It is a bridge to space, replacing the old ferry-boat rockets.

That's the main concept. What could be simpler? We have—perhaps an understatement—left out a number of 'engineering details,' but we will look at those next.

DESIGNING THE BEANSTALK.

Let us list some of the questions that we must answer before we have a satisfactory Beanstalk design. The most important ones are as follows:

• What shape should the load-bearing cable have?

• What materials will it be made from?

• Where will we get those materials?

• Where will we build the Beanstalk, where will we attach it to Earth, and how will we get it installed?

• How will we use the main cable to move materials up and down from Earth?

• Will a Beanstalk be stable, against the gravitational forces from the Sun and Moon, against weather, and against natural events here on Earth?

• What are the advantages of a Beanstalk over rockets?

• If we can get satisfactory answers to all these questions, *when* should we be able to build a

Beanstalk?

We can offer definite answers to some of these questions; other answers can only be conjectures. Let's begin with the first, which is also the easiest.

Suppose that the load-bearing cable is made of a single material. Then the most efficient design is one in which the stress on the material, per unit area, is the same all the way along it. This means there is no wasted strength. With such an assumption, it is a simple exercise in statics to derive an equation for the cross-sectional area of the cable as a function of distance from the center of the Earth.

The result has the form:

(1) $A(r) = A(R) . \exp(K.f(r/R).d/T.R)$

(*Note to Editor Baen. I know you told me not to use equations, but surely I'm entitled to at least one.*)

In this equation, $A(r)$ is the cross-sectional area of the cable at distance r from the center of the Earth, $A(R)$ is the area at the distance R of a geostationary orbit, K is the gravitational constant for the Earth, d is the density of the material from which the cable is made, T is the tensile strength of the cable per unit area, and $f(r/R) = 3/2 - R/r - (r/R)^2/2$.

Equation (1) tells us a great deal. First, we note that the variation of the cross-sectional area with distance does not depend on the tensile strength T directly, but only on the *ratio* T/d, which is the strength-to-weight ratio for the material. The substance from which we will build the Beanstalk must be strong, but more than that it should be strong and *light*.

Second, we can see that the shape of the cable is tremendously sensitive to the strength-to-weight ratio of the material, because this quantity occurs in the exponential of equation (1). To take a simple example, suppose that we have a material with a *taper factor* of 10,000. We define *taper factor* as the cross-sectional area of the cable at geostationary height, divided by the cross-sectional area at the surface of the Earth. So, for example, a cable that was one square meter in area at the bottom end would in this case be 10,000 square meters in area at geostationary height.

Now suppose that we could double the strength-to-weight ratio of the material we use for the cable. The taper ratio would drop from 10,000 to 100. If we could double the strength-to-weight ratio again, the taper ratio would reduce from 100 to 10.

It is clear that we should make the Beanstalk of the strongest possible material. Note that an infinitely strong material would need no taper at all.

Two other points are worth noting about the shape of the cable. It is easy to show that the function $f(r/R)$ has its maximum value at $r = R$. This confirms the intuitive result, that the cable must be thickest at geostationary height, where the load is greatest since the cable must support all the downward weight between that height and the surface of the Earth. Second, a look at the change of $f(r/R)$ with increasing r shows that the cross-sectional area decreases slowly above geostationary height. This is why we need a cable with a length that is much more than twice the distance to that height.

MATERIALS FOR THE BEANSTALK.

The cable that we need must be able to withstand a tension at least equal to its own weight from a height of 35,000 kilometers down to the surface. In practice, it must be a good deal stronger than that. We will certainly want to build in a reasonable safety factor, and we will want to hang other structures on the cable all the way down, to make it into a usable transportation system. So we expect that we will need to work with a very strong material, one with an unusually high strength-to-weight ratio. Of course, if one does not have a material that is quite as strong as needed, one can try and compensate by increasing the taper factor, but we have seen that this would be a very inefficient way to go. Halving the strength of materials would square the taper factor. The incentive to work with the strongest possible materials is very large.

The tension in the cable at a height of 35,770 kilometers, where upward and downward forces exactly balance, is less than the weight of a similar length of 35,770 kilometers of cable down here on Earth, for two reasons. The downward gravitational force decreases as the square of the distance from the center of the Earth, and the upward centrifugal force increases linearly with that distance. Both these effects tend to decrease the tension that the cable must support. A straightforward calculation shows that the maximum tension in a cable of constant cross-section will be equal to the weight of 4,940 kms. of such cable, here on Earth. This is in a sense a 'worst case' calculation, since we know that the cable will be designed to taper. However, the need for a safety factor means that we need to be conservative, and the figure of 4,940 kms. gives us a useful standard in terms of which we can calibrate the strength of available materials.

The definition we have chosen of a cable's strength, namely, how much length of its own substance it must support under Earth's gravity, is used quite widely. For a particular material, the length of itself the cable will support is called the 'support length' or 'characteristic length'. It is particularly handy because of the way in which the strength of materials is usually described, in terms of the tons *weight* per square centimeter (or per square inch) that they will support. (It would be more desirable, scientifically speaking, to give strength in dynes per square centimeter, or in newtons per square meter. These measures are independent of the Earth's surface gravity. But historically, pounds per square inch and kilos per square centimeter came first and things are still given that way in most of the handbooks. Note also that we are concerned only with *tensile* strength—how strong the material is when you pull it. *Compressive* and *shear* strengths are quite different, and a material may be very strong in compression and weak in tension. A building brick is a good example of this.)

Against our requirement of a support length of 4,940 kms, how well do the substances that we have available today measure up?

Not too well. Now we see why no one has yet built a Beanstalk. Table 1 shows the strengths of currently available materials, their densities, and their support lengths. (The physical data that I am using here is drawn, wherever possible, from the 'Handbook of Chemistry and Physics", 57th Edition. It is one of the most widely available reference texts and should be in any reasonable library.)

Not surprisingly, we won't be trying to make a

Beanstalk support cable from lead. As we can see from the table, even the best steel wire that we can find has a support length only one hundredth of what we need. The last entry in the table, Fictionite, would be perfect but for one drawback: it doesn't exist yet. The strongest materials that we have today, graphite and silicon carbide whiskers, still fall badly short of our requirements (for Earth, that is. A Mars Beanstalk has a minimum support length of only 973 kms. We could make one of those nicely using graphite whiskers).

Does this mean that we have a hopeless situation? It depends what confidence you have in the advance of technology. Table 2 lists the strength of materials that have been available at different dates in human history. There is some inevitable arbitrariness in making a table like this, since no one really knows when the Hittites began to smelt iron, and there must have been poor control of times, temperatures and purity of raw materials in the Bronze Age and early Iron Age. All these factors have a big effect on the tensile strength of the products.

It is tempting to try and fit some kind of function to the values in the table, and see when we will have a material available with a support length of 5,000 kms. or better. It is also very dangerous to even think of such a thing. For example, consider a fit to the data of the form: Strength $= B/(t - T)$, where B and T are to be determined by the data, and t is time in years before the year 2000 A.D. This fits the data fairly well if we choose $B = 525,000$ and $T = 17.5$ years. Unfortunately, such a form becomes infinite when $t = T$. If we were to believe such a fit, we would expect to have infinitely strong materials available to us some time in 1982!

TABLE 1
STRENGTH OF MATERIALS

Material	Tensile strength (kgms/squ.cm.)	Density (gms/c.c.)	Support length (kilometers)
Lead	200	11.4	0.18
Gold	1,400	19.3	0.73
Aluminum	2,000	2.7	7.4
Cast iron	3,500	7.8	4.5
Carbon steel	7,000	7.8	9.0
Manganese steel	16,000	7.8	21.
Drawn tungsten	35,000	19.3	18.
Drawn steel wire	42,000	7.8	54.
Iron whisker	126,000	7.8	161.
Silicon whisker (SiC)	210,000	3.2	660.
Graphite whisker	210,000	2.0	1,050.
Fictionite	2,000,000	2.0	10,000.

Not surprisingly, extrapolation of a trend without using physical models can lead us to ridiculous results. A much more plausible way of predicting the potential strength of materials is available to us,

TABLE 2
PROGRESS IN STRENGTH OF MATERIALS
AS A FUNCTION OF TIME

Year	Available material	Tensile Strength (kgms/sq.cm.)
1500 B.C.	Bronze	1,400
1850	Iron	3,500
1950	Special steels	16,000
1970	Drawn steel	42,000
1980	Graphite and silicon whiskers	210,000

Note: Years given indicate the dates when the materials could first be reliably produced in production quantities.

based on the known structure of the atom. In chemical reactions, only the outermost electrons of the atom participate, and it is the coupling of these outer electrons that decides the strength of chemical bonds. These bonds in turn set bounds on the possible strength of a material. Thus, so far as we are concerned the nucleus of the atom—which is where almost all the atomic mass resides—contributes nothing; strength of coupling, and hence material strength, comes only from those outer electrons.

In Table 3 we give the strengths of the chemical bonds for different pairs of atoms. These strengths, divided by the molecular weight of the appropriate element pair, decide the ultimate strength-to-weight ratio for a material entirely composed of

TABLE 3
POTENTIAL STRENGTH OF MATERIALS BASED ON THE STRENGTH OF CHEMICAL BONDS

Element pairs	Molecular weight*	Chemical bond strength (kcal/mole)	Support length (kilometers)*
Silicon-carbon	40	104	455
Carbon-carbon	24	145	1,050
Fluorine-hydrogen	20	136	1,190
Boron-hydrogen	11	80.7	1,278
Nitrogen-nitrogen	28	225.9	1,418
Carbon-oxygen	28	257.3	1,610
Hydrogen-hydrogen	2	104.2	9,118
Positronium-positronium	1/918.6	104	16,700,000

*Some of these element pairs do not exist as stable molecules, but can exist a crystal lattice structure.

**We are using the support length of the graphite whisker as the standard strength provided by the chemical bonds.

that pair of elements. The final column of the table shows the support length that this strength-to-weight ratio implies, using the carbon-carbon bond of the graphite whisker as the reference case.

Examining the Table, we see that the hydrogen-hydrogen bond has by far the greatest potential strength. In this bond, every electron participates in the bonding process (each atom has only one!) and the hydrogen nucleus contains no neutrons, which offer added weight without adding anything to the possible strength. A substance that consisted of pure solid hydrogen could in principle have a support length of more than 9,000 kilometers—very similar to the Fictionite of Table 1.

Even this strength is very modest if we are willing to look at a rather more exotic composition for our cables. Positronium is an 'atom' consisting of an electron and a positron. The positron takes the place of the usual proton in the hydrogen atom, but it has a far smaller mass. Positronium has been made in the laboratory, but it is unstable with a very short lifetime. If, however, positronium could be stabilized against decay, perhaps by the application of intense electromagnetic fields, then the resulting positronium-positronium bond should have a strength comparable with that of the hydrogen-hydrogen bond, and a far smaller molecular weight. It will have a support length of 16,700,000 kilometers—the taper of a Beanstalk made from such a material would be unmeasurably small. This would be true even for a Beanstalk on Jupiter, where the strength requirement is higher than for any other planet of the Solar System.

The positronium cable is likely to remain unavailable to us for some time yet. Even the solid hydrogen cable offers us the practical problem that we don't know how to build it. Rather than insisting on any particular material for our Beanstalk, it is safer and more reasonable to make a less specific statement: the strength of materials available to us has been increasing steadily throughout history, with the most striking advance coming in this century. It seems plausible to look for at least an increase of another order of magnitude in strength in the next hundred years. Such an advance in materials technology would make the construction of a Beanstalk quite feasible by the middle of the next century, at least from the point of view of strength of materials. It could come far sooner.

Something with the properties of Fictionite would do very nicely. The taper ration would be only 1.6, and a Beanstalk that was one meter in diameter at the lower end and of circular cross-section could support a load of nearly sixteen million tons.

WHERE TO BUILD THE BEANSTALK.

We have talked about what we will make the Beanstalk out of, but we have not discussed where we will find those materials. The answer to such a question is provided when we look at *how* we will build it.

For several reasons, the 'Tower of Babel' technique—start here on Earth and just build upwards—is not the way to go. The structure would be in *compression*, not tension, all the way up to beyond geostationary altitude, and we picked our material for its tensile strength. Worse still, structures in compression can buckle, which is a form of mechanical failure that does not apply to materials under tension.

Clearly, we will somehow begin *at the top*, with materials that we find up there. But *where* at the top? This is worth thinking about in more detail.

To a first approximation, the Earth is a sphere and its external gravity field is the same as that of a point mass. To a good second approximation, it is an oblate spheroid, with symmetry about the axis of rotation (the polar axis). The third order approximation gets much messier. Not only does the Earth "wobble" a bit about its axis of rotation, but there are fine inhomogeneities in the internal structure that show up as 'gravity anomalies' in the external gravitational field. These gravity anomalies are the deviations of the field from that which would be produced by a regular spheroid of revolution.

The anomalies are small—only a couple of milligals—but they are important. (In geodesy, a *gal* is not something that a male geodesist would like to snuggle up to; it is a unit of acceleration, equal to 1 cm. per second per second. A *milligal* is a thousandth of that. Earth's surface gravity is about 980 gals. If the Earth's gravity field were to change by one milligal, you would weigh differently by about one four-hundredth of an ounce. Even a change of a full gal—a thousand milligals—would not be noticed.)

If we look at these small gravity anomalies in the region of the orbit of a geostationary satellite, we find that they give rise to local maxima and minima of the gravitational potential. Satellites in such orbits tend to 'drift' to where the potential has its nearest local maximum, and to oscillate about such a position. For this particular location (35,770 kms. up, in the plane of the equator) these are the stable points of the gravitational field. At first sight, this looks like the best place to start to build your Beanstalk. You could put your source of materials there, and begin to extrude load-bearing cable up and down simultaneously, so as to keep a balance between the gravitational and centrifugal forces on the whole cable. Doing this, you might expect to be able to keep the cable Earth-stationary, always over the same fixed point of the surface.

Unfortunately, the gravitational potential is not so well-behaved. The positions of the stable points, the places where the potential has its local maxima, depend on the distance from the center of the Earth.

As you begin to extrude cable upwards and downwards, parts of the cable will move into regions where they are no longer at a local maximum of the potential. There will then be a strong tendency for the cable to "walk." It will begin to move steadily around the equator (and off the equator!), adjusting its position to the *average* of the gravity potential maxima encountered at all heights where a piece of the cable is present.

Such behavior is—at the very least—an annoyance. It means that you must allow for such motion in the design and construction, and you must tether the cable at the ground end when you have finished.

Such a tether is not a bad thing. We shall see later that it is an essential part of Beanstalk design if we want a usable structure, one that can carry cargo and people up and down it. However, you can't tether the Stalk until you have *finished* building it.

So we have still not answered the question, where do you do that construction? Remember, the geostationary location is full of other satellites—the communications satellites sit out there, and some of the weather satellites. It would be intolerable for the Beanstalk, half-built, to come drifting along through their *lebensraum* until it was finally long enough to tether.

What other options do we have? Well, there is the "bootstrap" method. In this, you fabricate a very thin Beanstalk, tether it, and use that to stop your main Beanstalk from wandering about during the construction.

My own favorite is more ambitious than a construction from geostationary orbit. You build *all* your Beanstalk well away from Earth, out at L-4 or L-5. When you have it all done, you fly it down. You arrange your timing so that the lower end arrives at a pre-prepared landing and tether site on the equator at the same time as the upper end makes a rendezvous with a ballast weight, way out beyond geostationary height. Once the Beanstalk has been tethered, the problem of a stable position for the orbit is not serious—it merely means that the Stalk doesn't follow the exact local vertical on the way up, because it tries to adapt to the mean gravity gradient all the way along its length.

Building the Stalk well away from Earth helps the problem of material supply. We certainly don't want to use Earth materials for construction, since getting them up there would be an enormous task. Fortunately, two of the promising substances that we found in the table of strong materials are graphite and silicon carbide. Coincidentally, two of the main categories of asteroid are termed the carbonaceous and the silicaceous types. They can be the source of our raw materials.

The way to build the Beanstalk is now apparent. We fly a smallish (a couple of kilometers in diameter) asteroid in from the Asteroid Belt and settle it at L-4. We build a solar power satellite or a fusion plant out there, too, to provide the energy that we need. Then we fabricate the Beanstalk, the whole thing: load-bearing cable, superconducting power cables, and drive train (more on these in a moment). And we fly it on down to Earth.

The final descent speed need not be high. We can use the inertia of the whole length of the Stalk to slow the arrival of its lower end.

The demand on the raw material resources of Earth in this whole operation will be minimal.

USING THE BEANSTALK.

A couple of paragraphs back, I threw in reference to superconducting power cables and drive train. These are the key to making the Beanstalk useful. Let us look in more detail at the whole structure of the Stalk.

We will have a load-bearing cable, perhaps a couple of meters across at the lower end, stretching up from the equator to out past geosynchronous altitude. It will be tethered at its lower end to prevent it from moving about around the Earth. It will be strong enough to support a load of millions of tons. What else do we need to do to make it useful?

First, we will strengthen the tether, to make sure that it can stand a pull of many millions of tons without coming loose from Earth. Next, we will go out to the far end of the cable, and hang a really big ballast weight there. The ballast weight pulls outwards, so that the whole cable is now under an added tension, balancing the pull of the ballast against the tether down on Earth.

We really need that tension.

Why? Well, suppose that we want to send a million tons of cargo up the Beanstalk. The first thing we will do is hang it on the cable near the ground tether. If the tension down near the lower end is a couple of million tons, when we hang the cargo on the cable we simply reduce the upward force on the tether from two million tons to one million tons. The cargo itself is providing some of the downward pull needed to balance the upward tug of the ballast at the far end. The whole system is still stable.

But if we had used a smaller ballast weight, enough to give us a pull at the tether of only half a million tons, we would be in trouble. If we hang a million tons of cargo on the cable, it will pull the ballast weight downwards. There is just not enough ballast to provide the required upward pull. We must provide an initial ballast weight that is sufficient to give a tension more than any weight that we will ever try and send up the cable.

There is another advantage to a massive ballast weight. We can use a shorter cable. We can hang a really big ballast at, say, a hundred thousand kilometers out, and it will not be necessary to have more cable beyond that point. The ballast weight provides the upward pull that balances the downward pull of the cable below geostationary height. We have to be a little careful here. A ballast that has a *mass* of ten million tons will not be enough to allow you to raise a *weight* of ten million tons up from Earth. The ballast will not pull outwards as hard as the weight pulls downwards, unless it is out at a distance where the net *outward* acceleration due to combined centrifugal and gravitational forces is one gee. This requires that the ballast be more than 1.8 million kilometers out from Earth—far past the Moon's distance of 400,000 kilometers.

We conclude from this that the ballast will be a massive one. This is no real problem. After all, even a modest sized asteroid, a kilometer across, will mass anything up to a billion tons.

Once we have a taut cable, suitably anchored, we need a power source for the activities on the Beanstalk. We put a solar power satellite or a fusion plant out at the far end and run cables all the way down, attaching them to the main loadbearing cable. Superconducting cables make sense, but we will have to be sure that they are suitably insulated—near-Earth space isn't *that* cold. But perhaps by the time we build the Stalk we will have superconductors that operate up to higher critical temperatures. The ones available now remain superconductors only up to about 23 degrees Kelvin.

There is a fringe benefit to running cables down the Beanstalk. We can carry down power from space without worrying about the effects of microwave radiation on the Earth—which is a serious worry with present solar power satellite designs.

Once we have the power cables installed, we can build the drive train, again attaching it to the load cable for its support. The easiest system for a drive train is probably a linear synchronous motor. The principles and the practice for that are well-established, which means it will all be off-the-shelf fixtures—except that we will want fifty to a hundred thousand kilometers of drive ladder. But remember, all this construction work will be done before we fly the Beanstalk in for a landing, and the abundant raw materials of the asteroid at L-4 will still be available to us.

Assuming that we drive cars up and down the Stalk at the uniform speed of 300 kilometers an hour, the journey up to synchronous altitude will take five days. That's a lot slower than a rocket, but it will be a lot more restful—and look at some of the other advantages.

First, we will have a completely non-polluting system, one that uses no reaction mass at all. This may appear a detail, until you look at the effects of frequent rocket launches on the delicate balance of the upper atmosphere and ionosphere of Earth.

Second, we will have a potentially *energy-free* system. Any energy that you use in the drive train in taking a mass up to synchronous height can in principle be recovered by making returning masses provide energy to the drive train as they descend to Earth. Even allowing for inevitable friction and energy conversion losses, a remarkably efficient system will be possible.

In some ways, the Stalk offers something even better than an energy-free system. When a mass begins its ascent from the surface of the Earth, it is moving with the speed of a point on the Earth's equator—a thousand miles an hour. When it reaches synchronous height, it will be travelling at 6,600 miles an hour. And if, from that point on, you let it "fall outwards" to the end of the Stalk, it will be launched on its way with a speed of more than 33,000 miles an hour, relative to the Earth. That's enough to throw it clear out of the Solar System.

Where did all the energy come from to speed up the mass?

The natural first answer might be, from the drive train. That is not the case. The energy comes from the rotational energy of the Earth itself. When you send a mass up the Beanstalk, you slow the Earth in its rotation by an infinitesimal amount, and when you send something back down, you speed it up a little. We don't need to worry about the effects on the planet, though. You'd have to take an awful lot of mass up there before you could make an appreciable effect on the rotation rate of Earth. The total rotational energy of Earth amounts to only about one thousandth of the planet's gravitational self-energy, but that is still an incredibly big number. We can use the Beanstalk without worrying about the effects that it will have on the Earth.

The converse of this is much less obvious. What about the effects of the Earth on the Beanstalk? Will we have to be worried about weather, earthquakes, and other natural events?

Earthquakes sound nasty. We certainly want the tether to be secure. If it came loose the whole Beanstalk would shoot off out into space, following the ballast. However, it is quite easy to protect ourselves. We simply arrange that the tether be held down by a mass that is itself a part of the lower end of the Stalk. Then the tether is provided by the simple weight of the bottom of the Beanstalk, and that will be a stable situation as long as the force at that point remains "down"—which will certainly be true unless something were to blow the whole Earth apart; in which case, we might expect to have other things to worry about.

Weather should be no problem. The Stalk presents so small a cross-sectional area compared with its strength that no storm we can imagine would trouble it. The same is true for perturbations from the gravity of the Sun and the Moon. Proper design of the Stalk will avoid any resonance effects, in which the period of the forces on the structure might coincide with any of its natural vibration frequencies.

In fact, by far the biggest danger we can conceive of is a man-made one—sabotage. A bomb, exploding halfway up the Beanstalk, would create unimaginable havoc in both the upper and lower sections of the structure. That would be the thing against which all security measures would be designed.

WHEN CAN WE BUILD A BEANSTALK?

We need two things before we can go ahead with a Beanstalk construction project: a strong enough material, and an off-Earth source of supplies. Both of these ought to be available in the next fifty to one hundred years. The general superiority of Beanstalks to rockets is so great that I expect to see the prototype built by the year 2050.

I do not regard this estimate as very adventuresome. It is certainly less so than Orville Wright's statement, when in 1911 he startled the world by predicting that we would eventually have passenger air service between cities as much as a hundred miles apart.

Unless we blow ourselves up, bog down in the Prox-mire, or find some other way to begin the slide back to the technological Dark Ages, normal engineering progress will give us the tools that we need to build a Beanstalk, by the middle of the next century. The economic impetus to deploy those tools will be provided by a recognition of the value of the off-Earth energy and raw materials, and it will be with us long before then.

This discussion seems to me to be so much a part of an inevitable future that I feel obliged to speculate a little further, just to make the subject matter less pedestrian. Let us look further out.

Non-synchronous Beanstalks have already been proposed for the Earth. These are shorter Stalks, non-tethered, that move around the Earth in low orbits and dip their ends into Earth's atmosphere and back out again a few times a revolution. They are a delightful and new idea that was developed in detail in a 1977 paper by Hans Moravec. The logical next step is free-space Beanstalks. These are revolving about their own center of mass, and they can be used to provide momentum transfer to spacecraft. They thus form a handy way to move materials about the Solar System.

Look ahead now a few thousand years. Civilization has largely moved off Earth, into free-space colonies. There are many thousands of these, each self-sustaining and self-contained, constructed from materials available in the Asteroid Belt. Although they are self-supporting, travel among them will be common, for commerce and recreation. Naturally enough, this travel will be accomplished without the use of reaction mass, via an extensive system of free-space Beanstalks which provide the velocity increases and decreases needed to move travellers around from colony to colony. There will be hundreds of thousands of these in a spherical region centered on the Sun, and they will all be freely orbiting.

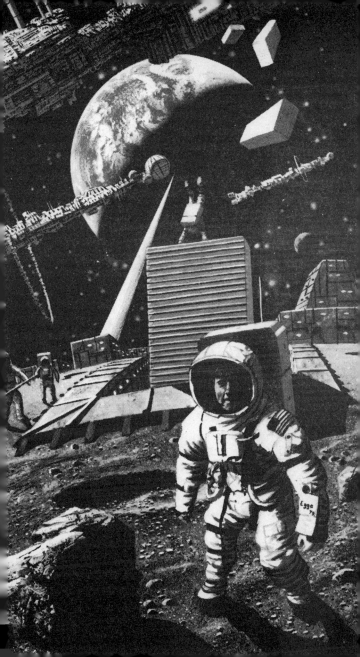

The whole civilization will be stable and organized, but there will be one continuing source of perturbation and danger. Certain singularities of the gravitational field exist, disturbing the movements of the colonists and their free transfer through the Solar System.

The singularities sweep their disorderly way around the Sun, upsetting the orbits of the colonies and the Beanstalks with their powerful gravity fields and presenting a real threat of capture to any who get too close to them.

It seems inevitable that, in some future Forum on one of the colonies, a speaker will one day arise to voice the will of the people. He will talk about the problem presented by the singularities, about the need to remove them. About the danger they offer, and about the inconvenience they cause. And finally, as a newly-arisen Cato he may mimic the words of his predecessor to pronounce judgment on one or more of those gravity singularities of the Solar System, the planets.

"Terra delenda est"—Earth must be destroyed!

BEANSTALK TIME—A FINAL NOTE.

Beanstalks, originally called skyhooks, are an idea of the 1960's whose time may at last have come. They are used as important elements of at least two novels published in 1979, Arthur Clarke's "The Fountains Of Paradise" and my own "The Web Between The Worlds." I suspect that they will become a standard element of most projected futures, as a rational alternative to the rocketry that has served sf writers so long and so well. •

THE END.

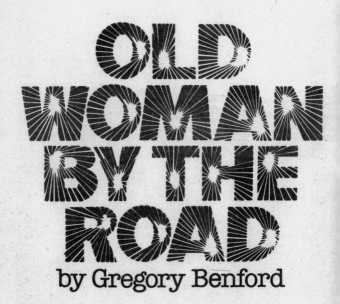

OLD WOMAN BY THE ROAD

by Gregory Benford

Up to now, most examinations of space colonies have been rather starry-eyed, if not downright fatuous: power for the powerless, that sort of thing. Well, power doesn't flow that way...

An old woman in a formless, wrinkled dress and worn shoes sat at the side of the road. A soft wind sighed through the pines crowding the white strip of road and I was panting from the fast pace I was keeping. The old woman was sitting there, silent and unmoving. I nearly walked by before I saw her.

"You're resting?" I said.

"Waiting." Her voice was dry and when she breathed out there was a sound in her throat like rustling leaves. She was sitting on a brown cardboard suitcase with copper latches. It was cracked along the side and white cloth stuck out.

"For the bus?"

"For Buck."

"The copter said the bus will stop up around the bend," I said. "On the main road."

"I know."

"It won't come down this side road."

I was late myself and I figured she had picked the wrong spot to wait.

"Buck will be along." Her voice was high and had the back country twang in it. My own voice had some of the same sound but I was keeping my vowels flat right now and her accent reminded me of how far I had come.

I looked down the long curve of the sandy road. A pickup truck growled out of a side road and into the deep ruts of white sand. People were riding in the back along with some boxes and trunks and a 3D. They were taking everything valuable they could, but the Outskirters hadn't given us much time.

"Who's Buck?"

"My dog." She looked at me directly, as though it was obvious who Buck was.

"Look, the bus — "

"You're the Bishop boy, aren't you?"

I looked off up the road again. That set of words *the Bishop boy* was like a grain of sand caught between my back teeth. My mother's friends had used that phrase when they came over for an evening of bridge, before I went away to the university. There never seemed to be any way to avoid admitting it and then putting myself in a little slot in other people's heads. There hadn't been any way then and there wasn't one now. I said, "Yes, I am." The words came out precisely.

"Thought so."

"You're — ?"

"Elizabeth McKenzie."

"Ah."

We had done the ritual so now we could talk.

"I knew your grandmother real well."

"Mrs. McKenzie — "

"I 'strictly believe I saw you once, long time ago. Out at one of your grandmother's fish fries. You and some little boys were playing with the nets down by the water. My husband went to shoo you away from the boats. I was cleaning flounders and your grandfather was tending the fire. It was down at Point Clear."

"I think I remember that. Mrs. McKenzie, there's not long before the last bus."

"I'm waiting for Buck."

"Where is he?"

"He ran off in the woods."

I worked my backpack straps around on my shoulders. They creaked in the quiet.

There wasn't a lot of time left. Pretty soon now it would start. One of the big reflecting mirrors up in synchronous Outskirter orbit would focus its light on a rechargable tube of gas. The gas would pass through its molecular phases and be excited by the incident light. Then the lasing process would begin in the long tube, excited molecules cascading down together from one preferentially occupied quantum state to another lower state, the traveling wave jarring more photons loose as it swept down the tube. The photons would add in phase, summing in an intense wave, growing in amplitude. The beam that came out of the hundred meter long tube would slice down through the atmosphere and through the cloud cover above us. And instead of striking an array of layered solid state collectors outside Mobile, the beam would cut a swath twenty meters wide through the trees and fields around us.

"The bus is coming," I said.

She looked at me.

"I'll carry that suitcase for you."

"I can manage it." She squinted off into the distance and I saw she was tired, tired beyond knowing it.

"I'll go along with you, Mrs. McKenzie."

"I'm not going until Buck comes on back."

"The bus . . . Leave that dog, Mrs. McKenzie."

"I don't need that blessed bus."

"Why not?"

"My children drove off to Mobile a few hours back with their families. They said they'd be coming to pick me up."

"My insteted radio — " I gestured at my temple — "says the roads to Mobile are jammed up. You can't count on them getting back."

She moved her thin legs on the suitcase. "My children left early."

"Well — "

"They're dropping off a lot of the things they had from that new house of theirs. Then they'll come back and get me. They said so."

"How'll they know where you are?"

"I tole 'em I'd try to walk to the main road. Got tired, is all." She blinked at the sun. "They'll know I'm back in here."

"Just the same, the deadline — "

"I'm all right, don't you mind. They're good children, grateful for all I've gone and done for them."

"I think it's better if you get on the bus, Mrs. McKenzie."

"I'm not going without Buck. Buck has been with me since he was a . . ." She didn't finish and I looked around at the pine woods, blinking back sweat. In among the pines were some oak, their roots bulging up out of the sandy soil and knotted. There were a lot of places for a dog to be. The land around here was flat and barely above sea level. I had come down to Baldwin County to camp and rest. I'd been here five days, taking skiffs down the Fish River, looking for the places I'd been when I was a boy and my grandmother had rented boats on the river and lived in an old rambling fisherman's house. The big mysterious island I remembered and called Treasure Island, smack in the middle of Fish River, was now a soggy stand of trees in a bog. The steady currents had swept it away. There was thick mud there now and the black water tasted like a weak leaf tea. But it was all fine, the inlets and the deep river currents that pulled on the skiff. I'd been camping down on the point where the Fish River snaked around before running down in a straight line into the bay. The helicopter that came over in the morning blaring out the alert woke me up. The Outskirters had given four hours warning, the recording said. This forty-klick square in southern Alabama, and two others in Asia, had been picked out at random for a reprisal. The big cylinder communities circling Earth would use their laser systems, designed for power transfer from orbit, to slash and burn. The carving would go on until Earth granted the cylinder worlds real independence. But there was no real balance of power there. Once the Outskirters had a free hand they could hold the leash on Earth. They had the economic and now the military power. And maybe that wasn't so bad; they were the best people Earth could produce.

I had been thinking about that a lot while I was down on the point. It was hard to figure which side you should be on. There were fine people up in orbit and they were a lot like me. A lot more than the people in Baldwin County, anyway, even though I'd grown up here. I'd worked on laser tech systems for a while now and I knew the real future was up in orbit. The Outskirters were smart and they knew when to act.

"Where's Buck?" I said decisively.

"He . . . that way." A weak wave of the hand.

I wrestled my backpack into the shoulder of the road where the creeper grass took hold. A car wheezed its way out of a rutted side road. Pale, crowded faces with big eyes looked out at us and then the driver hit the hydrogen and they got out of there.

I went into the short pines near the road. Sand flies jumped where my boots struck. The white sand made that soft *skree* sound as my boots skated over it. I remembered how I'd first heard that sound down here as a kid, wearing tennis shoes, and how I'd finally figured out what caused it.

"Buck!"

There was a flash of brown over to the left and I went after it. I ran through a thick stand of pine and the dog yelped and took off, dodging under a blackleaf bush. I called it again. The dog didn't even slow down. I skirted to the left. He went into some oak scrub and I could hear him getting tangled in it and then getting free and out the other side. By that time he was fifty meters away and moving fast.

When I got back to the old woman she didn't seem to notice me. "I can't catch Buck, Mrs. McKenzie."

"Knew you wouldn't." She grinned at me, a grin with real mirth in it. "Buck is a fast one."

"Call him."

She smiled vacantly and raised her hands to her mouth. "Buck! Here boy!"

The low pine trees swallowed the sound.

"Must of run off."

"Now, Mrs. — "

"You scared him. He doesn't come when there are some around he don't know."

"There isn't time to wait for him."

"I'm not leaving without ole Buck. Times I was alone down on the river at the old McAllister place and the water would come up under the house. Buck was the only company I had. Only soul I saw for five weeks in that big blow we had."

A low whine. "I think that's the bus."

She cocked her head. "I hear something all right."

"Come on. I'll carry your suitcase."

She curled her lip up and crossed her arms. "My children will be by for me. I told them to look for me along in here."

"Your children might not make it back in time."

"They're loyal children."

"Mrs. McKenzie, I can't wait for you to be reasonable." I picked up my backpack and brushed off some red ants crawling on the straps. "You walked this far from the McAllister place?" I swung the pack onto one arm and then the other.

"I did."

The old McAllister place was a good five klicks away. So she had gotten exhausted and sat down here to rest.

"Reasonable. You Bishops was always the reasonable ones." She narrowed her eyes. There were a lot of memories in her face.

"That's why I want you to go now."

"Your grandma was always talking about you." She glanced skyward. "You been up there, hadn't you?"

"Yes. Yes, I have."

"An' you're goin' back. You were down here on vacation."

I looked down the road, deserted now.

"It's your people, up there."

"The wrong group seems to be in control."

"Same people as always." She sniffed.

"Mrs. McKenzie, there's the bus." The turbo made its high whirr as it wheeled off the blacktop highway around the bend. "It's the last one."

"You go along." She sat back heavily on the suitcase. I reached out to take her arm and her face changed. "Don't touch me, boy."

I saw that she wouldn't let me coax or force her down that last bend. She had gone as far as she was going to and the world would have to come the rest of the distance itself.

Up ahead the bus driver was probably behind schedule for this last pickup. He was going to be irritated and more than a little scared. The Outskirters would come in right on time, he knew that.

I ran. The sand gave way under me. I saw I was more tired than I thought by the running and walking I had done to get here. I ploughed through the deep ruts. The whole damned planet was dragging at my feet, holding me down. I went about two hundred meters along the bend, nearly within view of the bus, when I heard it start up with a rumble. I ran faster and tasted sweat. The driver raced the engine, in a hurry. He had to come toward me as he swung out onto Route 80 on the way back to Mobile. Maybe I could make it to the highway in time for him to see me and slow down. I knew everything depended now on how fast I could move so I put my head down and ran.

Ran.

But there was the old woman back there. To get her the driver would have to take the bus down that rutted road in the sand and risk getting stuck. All that to get the old woman with the grateful children. She didn't seem to understand that there were ungrateful children in the skies now, she didn't seem to understand much of what was going on, and suddenly I wasn't so sure I did either.

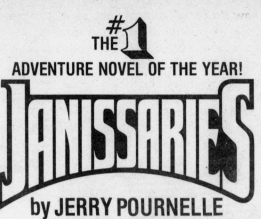

Defending The Third Industrial Revolution

by G. Harry Stine

By the year 2015 A.D., space utilization will have progressed to the point where there are many large multi-purpose communications/information satellites in geosynchronous orbit, a wide variety of space manufacturing facilities in various earth and lunar orbits, as many as two dozen or more huge solar power satellites beaming power from geosychronous orbit to both earth and the various space industrial facilities, and several lunar outposts set up to mine lunar materials. This is all part of "the Third Industrial Revolution," the utilization of space for the benefit of people on earth. This Third Industrial Revolution is now the subject of intense study and planning by both government agencies and private enterprise in several countries around the world.

The Third Industrial Revolution is already under way. It began on April 6, 1965 with the launching of "Early Bird," the world's first commercial communications satellite. The 1970s is the decade of the communications satellite; the 1980s promises to usher in the development of space processing — the manufacture in earth orbit of the first of many industrial products that can be made only in the weightlessness of earth orbit. The 1990s should see the first solar power satellites.

Both domestic and international private enterprise is involved. Already the Soviet Union has conducted intensive experimentation in space processing aboard various *Soyuz* and *Soyuz-Salyut* missions. They continue as of this writing.

The Third Industrial Revolution is going to create two areas of concern and interest to military planners in the next thirty to fifty years.

One of these is new technology that will create new problems of defense and military operations. Space industrialization will produce new and less expensive space transportation systems. Space industrialization will produce radically new materials that will have military implications in terms of increased strength, decreased weight, and various other physical properties. Space industrialization will also produce very large energy collectors and transmission devices in space.

The second area of concern involves the fact that the Third Industrial Revolution will create property of value in space—communications satellites, information-handling satellites, manned space laboratories, manned and unmanned space factories, solar power satellites, lunar mining stations and outposts, lunar and orbital catapults or "mass drivers," and other facilities. There will be human activity in space connected with each of these. These facilities will also have commercial value, property value, and even military threat value. Where there exist arenas of human activity and inter-relationships and property, there will be disagreements and conflict. We cannot expect these aspects of human nature to change in the next fifty years.

Therefore as we go into space we will have to take

our highly-evolved cultural heritages and societal organizations with us to forestall disagreements and to resolve conflicts. There are the rules, codes, regulations, laws, and treaties that we have individually and collectively agreed to observe. But they are effective only when the majority of people involved agree to abide by them, and when means exist to enforce compliance with them.

These means of enforcement include the military police organizations. There is a very fine line of distinction between a military organization and a police organization. In some cultures and nations, the distinction cannot be drawn at all. In our Anglo-American culture, the police handle the affairs of internal compliance while the military organization handles the enforcement of trans-national agreements including protection of property from seizure or destruction by other nations.

Therefore, the Third Industrial Revolution is not only going to require military/police protection of space property but will present military organizations with new technology. Both of these involve new military doctrines for use in earth-luna space . . . or cis-lunar space, that being the portion of space that exists between the Planet Earth and the orbit of its satellite, the Moon.

Protection of space property is very dependent upon the basic military rationales, doctrines, and operational realities of cis-lunar celestial mechanics. Celestial mechanics involves the way objects move in space with relationship to various gravitational fields. It is no longer a subject for mere academic discussion or scientific utility in aiming space probes. Celestial mechanics becomes the cornerstone of space strategic and tactical doctrines.

There will be military operations in space above and beyond those necessary for protection of space properties.

Historians Will and Ariel Durant have pointed out, "In every century the generals and rulers (with rare exceptions like Ashoka and Augustus) have smiled at the philosophers' timid dislike of war . . . War is one of the constants of history, and has not diminished with civilization or democracy. In the last 3,421 years of recorded history, only 268 have seen no war."

Anthropologist Dr. Carleton S. Coon has succinctly summarized the prevailing philosophy of the majority of the peoples (and therefore their governments) of the world in what he terms the "Neolithic philosophy: You stay in your village and I will stay in mine. If your sheep eat our grass we will kill you, or we may kill you anyhow to get all the grass for our own sheep. Anyone who tries to change our ways is a witch and we will kill him. Keep out of our village!" This Neolithic philosophy was successful for its time as an attempt to cope with a world where shortages and outright lack of basic survival necessities have been the norm. It created the "Atilla Syndrome," a least-effort way of acquiring what one wants and does not have: "Take it by force."

The rational antithesis of the Atilla Syndrome has existed only briefly in recent history. It came into being about 250 years ago as a philosophical buttress to the First Industrial Revolution and it was a better least-effort solution: "Make it, don't take it, and everybody has more." This may be termed "The Industrial Syndrome."

Until the Neolithic philosophy of Coon disappears from the human race (if it ever does; it may be an important long-term survival trait), it would be folly to believe that mankind will disarm and settle all disputes by negotiation. The arts of diplomacy and politics are not yet rigorous enough to prevent us from killing each other all of the time . . . just some of the time. It is a very delicate evolving system that requires the lubrication of learned responses and manners. It is very susceptible to sand thrown in the works by charismatic leaders, "men on horseback." Its effectiveness is supported only by the veiled threat of physical force that could or might be brought to bear should diplomacy fail.

Until we manage to eradicate the Neolithic philosophy and its Atilla Syndrome from the majority of the human race—if we ever do—there will be military implications to everything we do, like it or not.

This led to late pioneer futurist, Dandridge M. Cole, to formulate in 1960 his famous "Panama Theory" of the military utilization of space. This theory is briefly stated:

"There are strategic areas in space—vital to future scientific, military, and commercial space programs—which could be excluded from our use through occupation and control by unfriendly powers. This statement is based on the assumption that in colonizing space, man (and/other intelligent beings) will compete for the more desirable areas . . ."

When this is applied to military space operations in the Earth-Moon system, the prime strategic doctrine is that of the "gravity well."

The gravity well is a concept first put forth by Dr. Robert S. Richardson, then of Mount Wilson Observatory, and reported by Arthur C. Clarke in his pioneering 1950 book on space, *Interplanetary Flight*. Because of Earth's gravity field, our planet can be considered as being at the bottom of a tapering well some 4000 miles deep. Near the bottom of the well, the walls are very steep; as one reaches the top of the "gravity well," the sides become less steep until, at the top of this funnel, we have reached a nearly flat plain which is dimpled by another, smaller, shallower gravity well some 240,000 miles away, the gravity well of the Moon. While this is a simplification, it conveys the concept of the gravity well.

To climb up the gravity well from the planetary surface requires a great deal of energy. Partway up the gravity well, it is possible to maintain the position of an object by making it spin around the surface of the funnel rapidly enough so that centrifugal force neatly balances the gravitational force tending to pull the object back to the planet at the bottom of the funnel. To get away from the earth, one must project an object such as a space vehicle up the side of the gravitational well at an initial speed of 7 miles per second; it then climbs the walls of the well and, if its direction and speed are just right, crosses the nearly level plain at the top until it falls into the gravity well of the Moon. Or goes on outward into the Solar System, in which case our gravity well model must be expanded to include the very powerful gravity well of the Sun. But since we are considering only the Earth-Moon system herein, the simple model will suffice.

The strategic implications of the gravity well in

military space operations require that one be at the top of a gravity well or at least higher up the well than the adversary.

The planet-bound analogy to this is the doctrine of the "high ground." In naval tactics during the age of sail, it was the "wind gauge"; or getting upwind of the enemy.

The salient feature of the gravity well doctrine is the fact that it provides both an energy advantage and a maneuvering advantage to the person on the high ground. It requires far less energy in the form of propulsion and propellants to operate high on the gravity well, and it is possible to maneuver with relative ease and flexibility at or near the top of it.

A simple analogy indicates the basic military advantage: Put one man at the bottom of a well and the other at the top of a well. Give them both rocks to throw at each other. Which man is going to get hurt? Which man has more time to see his opponent's rocks coming and more opportunity to get out of the way? Which man has the greater opportunity to do something about the oncoming rock?.

In Earth-Moon orbital space the person having a base of maneuver on top of a deep gravity well or in a shallower gravity well than his opponent has a definite military advantage in terms of surveillance capability, energy required to affect a strike, maneuvering room, and the ability to activate countermeasures in reasonable time.

The logical consequence of the gravity well doctrine leads inevitably to the most important military fact of the late 20th Century and the early 21st Century: With improvements in space transportation available and with the technology in hand to maintain long-term military positions in space, the

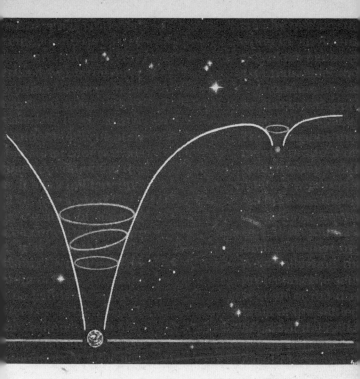

A representation of the gravity wells of the Earth-Moon system. A gravity well can be thought of as a funnel-shaped pit with a celestial body at the bottom. To get out of a gravity well, one must project a space vehicle up the wall of the gravity well with enough velocity to get over the edge. To orbit around the sides of the gravity well funnel, a spacecraft must be given enough velocity for the centrifugal force to balance the pull of gravity.

control of the Moon means control of the Earth. In a like manner, according to this doctrine, *control of the L4 and L5 libration points in the lunar orbit means control of the Earth-Moon system.*

Control implies that one is able to regulate the flow of space-going commerce and other traffic, to protect one's own facilities in space, to deny the use of other critical military *and/or* commercial orbital areas to others, to launch strikes against *any* target on the surface of the Earth *or* the Moon or in any orbit in the Earth-Moon system, or to detect any oncoming threat and take counteraction in time.

The gravity well doctrine dictates the general considerations for space weapons systems that would be most effective. However, one must first take a careful look at the basic concept of a weapon.

A weapon can be broadly defined as a means of imposing one's will upon another. Thus, a weapon need not have a physical reality; the threat of the use of a weapon is itself a weapon—if the opponent believes the said weapon exists and will be used.

Heinlein defines a weapon as a machine for the manipulation of energy. But it has a broader definition than that. The following categorization of weapons may be useful in determining those that would be most useful in various operational zones of the Earth-Moon system and may also provide a key to the discovery of new and heretofore unsuspected space weapons that could be developed and used with the technology of the Third Industrial Revolution.

Mass manipulators: Produce damage through the use of the basic inertial characteristics of mass

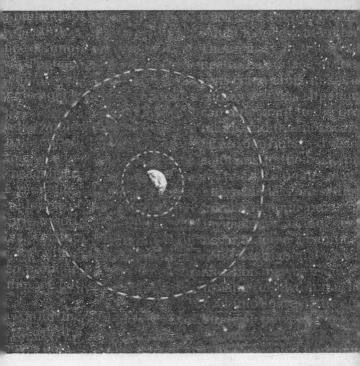

The various military operational areas of the Earth-Moon system, not to scale. Near-Earth Orbit extends from an altitude of about 50 kilometers above the Earth out to about 200 kilometers. Cis-Lunar Space extends from 200 kilometers to the orbit of the Moon. Lunar Surface/Orbit extends from the surface of the Moon to about 100 kilometers above the Moon. And Translunar Space extends from the orbit of the Moon outwards to about a million kilometers where the gravity field of the Sun dominates spacecraft motion.

and the conversion of energy of position (potential energy) to energy of motion (kinetic energy): mass projectors, penetrators, detectors, and decoys.

Energy manipulators: Produce damage through the application of high energy density or the sudden release of large amounts of energy: projectors, concentrators, releasers, screens, and detectors.

Biological manipulators: Produce damage to organic life forms or other chemical agents: gases, poisons, disease vectors, etc.

Psychological manipulators: Produce alteration of the mental state of the enemy in a desirable fashion that reduces the will or capability to resist: propaganda, counterintelligence, brain-washing, covert manipulation of the information media, mood-altering drugs, consciousness-altering drugs, mind-altering drugs.

Some weapons are a combination of one or more of these basic types, and some require a vehicle to transport them to the point of use or application.

Use of these weapons in accordance with the strategic doctrine of the gravity well requires in turn that we consider the Earth-Moon system to consist of a series of definite military operational areas. These are basically zones within the gravity well or, for a better mental view, a series of concentric spheres with the Earth at the center. These are no so much well-defined spheres with distinct boundaries, but rather zones of operation that fade into one another. In a sense, they resemble the energy levels of electrons around an atomic nucleus. Briefly, these zones may be defined as:

Near Earth Orbit (NEO) extending from an arbitrary level of 50 kilometers above the Earth's surface to approximately 200 kilometers—well below the lower limits of the Van Allen radiation belts.

Cis-lunar Space (CLS) extending from about 200 kilometers above the Earth's surface to the geosynchronous orbital altitude of about 39,000 kilometers.

Lunar Surface/Orbit (LSO) extending from geosynchronous orbit to the lunar orbit about the Earth and including the *Near Lunar Orbits* with an arbitrary altitude of about 100 kilometers from the lunar surface.

Translunar Space (TLS) extending from the lunar orbit out to an arbitrary distance of approximately one million kilometers from the surface of the Earth at which distance an object can be considered to be in orbit around the Sun due to the much greater influence of the solar gravity field at that distance.

Each operational area has unique military considerations that affect tactical doctrine, tactical operations, and weapons systems within each area.

Near Earth Orbit is a valuable military operational area for earth-launched, earth-oriented activities and of course is already being used as such; it is an area that is easily reached from the earth's surface by spacecraft capable of attaining velocities of about 25,000 feet per second. So far during this decade at least six nations have begun conducting reconaissance and surveillance operations there—and at least two nations operate manned spacecraft in the area. In the years to come NEO could be used for quick-look and high-detail surveillance, satellite hunter-killer operations, a staging area for manned surface-to-surface troop strike transports, and "quick dip" hypersonic skimming into the upper atmosphere for surveillance, reconaissance, or offensive purposes. Thus, NEO is basically a tactical scouting area for earth-centered operations and a maneuvering area for surface-to-surface operations. It is also the area through which surface-to-surface ICBM's must travel during the ballistic portion of their flight and therefore the area in which they are most vulnerable to intercept by orbital-launched interceptors or orbital beam weapons. Although NEO is reasonably far up on the sides of the gravity well funnel in terms of the energy requirements needed to reach the area from the earth's surface, current technology permits the deployment of rapid-ascent satellite interceptors. Thus NEO is an area where it is difficult to respond to threat: a nearness to counter-weapons on the surface or in orbit, and large energy expenditures are required for maneuver in the area. The possibility of basing a large manned military space station in NEO should be dismissed; it would be a very large target in a predictable trajectory and would be destroyed in the opening moments of any war in which its presence could be a factor.

Cis-lunar space, however is a more valuable zone of maneuver and reconaissance. Not only is less energy required for maneuver but geosynchronous orbit lies in CLS, making it a prime location for surveillance, navigational, communications, data transfer, meteorological, and energy satellites. Geosynchronous orbit is already crowded. As of mid-1977, there were more than a hundred unmanned satellites located in geosynchronous orbit. Because of orbital crowding and the possibility of frequency interference caused by beam overlapping, these numerous small satellites will be replaced in the late 1980s and the 1990s with large, multi-purpose platforms which will be militarily vulnerable.

However, facilities in CLS are more secure from earth-launched offensive operations because of the time required for vehicles to climb the gravity well. Various location and detection systems sited in NEO and CLS may be used to identify any potential threat with sufficient early-warning time to permit initiation of counter-activities.

The primary consideration of CLS from the military point of view is the strategic importance of the trojan libration points in the lunar orbit. More of this later.

Lunar surface/orbit has quite different military characteristics. Because of the mass of Luna, it is a prime location for a military base on or probably beneath its surface. It is the prime location for one of the most important space weapons systems we can now foresee, a weapon system that is basically very old. This device is the catapult, usually referred to in current terminology as a "mass driver." Whatever term is used to identify it, it is a rock-thrower. The Moon is the best site in the Earth-Moon system for such a device because the mass of the Moon provides ample ammunition for the mass driver as well as a very large and stable base to improve its accuracy. Launching very large masses at speeds of a mile per second or more produces some massive reaction forces which would misalign or reorient any mass driver located on its own in orbital space.

The lunar mass driver is a critical system requirement for the overall industrialization of the Earth-Moon system. Although an Earth-based mass driver is a potential commercial cargo transportation system for terrestrial materials launched into space, the energy requirements are very large because of the Earth's atmosphere and the very deep gravity well; the lunar mass driver is the most economical cargo transportation device now envisioned for providing materials for space industrialization, including the materials to construct large space structures. It will undoubtedly be built in several locations on the lunar surface for providing lunar materials for deep space operations in the Earth-Moon system. However, it has a military utility that cannot and must not be overlooked.

A large lunar mass driver capable of hurling masses of up to one ton can be converted into an earth bombardment system. It is a non-nuclear weapon and not subject to existing UN treaties! The results of the sudden dissipation of large amounts of kinetic energy should not be lightly dismissed. The Barringer Meteor Crater in Arizona was created by the impact of an estimated 80-foot diameter nickel-iron meteorite; the impact was roughly equivalent to the detonation of 2,500,000 tons of TNT—read that as a 2.5 megaton bomb.

Small lunar mass drivers can be used as weapons systems against space facilities. Such small mass drivers can be considered as space Gatling guns. Such a small mass driver is envisioned as throwing a mass of a couple of kilograms, but throwing such small masses in very rapid succession. The impact of a one kilogram mass travelling at several miles per second can do considerable damage to a space facility—such as when several hundred or thousand such masses impact a solar power satellite, the irridescent solar panels of a reconaissance satellite, or the pressure hull of a manned space

station.

No explosives are required for such space weapons; the conversion of kinetic energy to heat is quite sufficient.

The military capabilities of mass drivers built and used for commercial purposes are such that they will require protection against seizure or destruction, wherever they are built and operated.

The area of military operations beyond the lunar orbit that we have tagged "Translunar Space" is a zone of maneuver and rendezvous for military space vehicles with very large propulsion and maneuvering capabilities. There is a location in this area, however, that could be used as a military staging point. Beyond the Moon's orbit along the Earth-Moon line lies a zone in space where the gravity fields of both the Earth and the Moon balance one another; this is known as the L2 lunar libration point. Anything placed at the L2 point will stay there, hidden from view of anyone on the surface of the Earth or on the earthside of the Moon.

There are two other locations in the Earth-Moon system that are of the utmost military importance. These are the so-called "trojan" lunar libration points. They are the result of a special and unique solution to the classical "three body" problem in celestial mechanics. There is a zone in the Moon's orbit 60-degrees behind or following the Moon in the orbit and 60 degrees ahead of the Moon; these are stable points where the gravity field of the Earth and the Moon are balanced or equalled-out. An object placed in either of these two libration points—labeled L4 and L5 for convenience—will stay there. L4 and L5 are the two most stable of the libration points in the Earth-Moon system.

The importance of the L4 and L5 libration points from a military viewpoint is the fact that neither has a gravity well and both sit at the top of the gravity wells of both the Earth and the Moon. From the L4/L5 points, one can control the gravity wells of the entire Earth-Moon system.

These libration points have no gravity wells. A zero gravity well means the greatest capability for maneuver with the minimum amount of energy and denies the use of a gravity well to an adversary for his purposes.

At L4/L5, one sits on top of the hill, so to speak. These points are the most difficult places to reach in the Earth-Moon system from the energy expenditure point of view. They are therefore the best places to site any military bases because they are defensible. They are the best locations for small mass drivers and high-energy beam weapons.

L4/L5 are proposed as the locations of large future space settlements by O'Neill and the L5 Society. Nowhere in the extensive literature about this proposal is there to be found any discussion of the military implications of these L4/L5 sites. If the military implications were considered, they were either dismissed as unimportant or simply ignored for philosophical/ideological reasons.

There is no guarantee that any space settlements at the L4/L5 locations—or on the Moon either, for that matter—will remain peaceful industrial or commercial activities. Writers such as Heinlein and Bova have already speculated on scenarios involving revolutions and seizures of such space settlements. There are any number of grievances that can and have triggered military uprisings. There

The Earth-Moon system, drawn to scale, showing the relative locations of geosynchronous orbit, the Moon, and the five lunar libration points. Libration points L1, L2, and L3 are considered to be "unstable" because some energy will have to be expended to maintain an object at these locations. However, the L4 and L5 libration points are "stable."

DESTINIES

are any number of reasons or lessons from history wherein an industrious, hard-working group of close-knit people have taken a sharp turn in their external affairs to become a military threat.

And there are any number of scenarios that can be developed around the seizure and takeover of a large L4/L5 space settlement for military reasons. These reasons might include control of the settlement's product of value—energy or materials—or straightaway military control of the facility to exert military pressure on nations on Earth.

There are therefore two roles for military space operations involving the space settlements at L4/L5: (a) military protective force or presence, similar to that of the U.S. Army in the American West following the Civil War, for the purpose of protecting the settlements against takeover or prevention of the use of military force by the inhabitants of the settlements, or (b) straightforward use of part of the L4/L5 space settlements as an admitted military base of operations for control of the Earth-Moon system.

This last will be argued vehemently. However, are we very certain that the space settlements under consideration will be built or even occupied forever by the sort of hard-working, industrious, peace-loving Anglo-American types now envisaged as populating these settlements by advocates?

One must point out that there are social characteristics of many basically militant Oriental cultures that would make their people optimum space settlers, characteristics such as the ability to live in high-density quarters with little or no privacy, subjugation of the individual to the group, highly structured manners and other inter-personal interfaces, and unquestioning willingness of the individual to follow the directives of authority figures. The military in these cultures now lies barely beneath the surface of the culture, hidden from recent conquerors in some cases.

How will this situation be handled? The author can only point to the problem. It will take the best minds and the most careful diplomacy of the next fifty to one hundred years to begin to find workable solutions to the basic problem.

The L4/L5 points may be declared demilitarized international zones; this may work for a time, but from a historic point of view, treaties are rarely inviolate for as long as fifty years and practically never in force a century after their signing.

By international agreement, a balance of power situation may be established with adversaries controlling the two lunar libration points in a carryover into space of the current USA-USSR balance of strategic power.

We may also find that the Third Industrial Revolution takes into space many of the current industrial security activities that surround most business operations in a quiet, unobtrusive, but highly effective manner. The military may indeed be present in space as they already are. There may also be another type of organization in space connected with space industrialization: a police force, the security guard, and company cops.

It is often easier to get into a secure military base than it is to gain access to a factory. Industrial security is much more stringent than military security; this is a statement of observed fact.

We may find that firms involved in space industrialization would rather hire mercenaries than depend upon military protection from a government. Firms such as Brinks, Wells Fargo, Purolator, and other private security organizations may end up in space along with many of the industrial firms they presently protect.

Each advance of humanity into new and different environments has created new types of social organizations to handle the new problems presented by the advance. Our expansion into space in the Third Industrial Revolution is no exception. We are beginning to see the development of new types of social organization to handle the knotty problems of raising large amount of capital to finance high-risk, long-term projects such as solar power satellites. The Third Industrial Revolution presents other difficult problems, as we have seen. We must therefore anticipate the development of new types of military organizations that might evolve to handle the very difficult problems arising from the military implications of our expansion into space.

We cannot ignore the reality of the military implications of space any more than we can ignore the reality of our home town lives by disbanding the town police force. We can attempt to build a universe of law where matters of human conflict can be solved by judgment, arbitration or negotiation. But this universe of law must be backed up by the means to enforce the rules through application of physical coercion. This will always be the case as long as the Atilla Syndrome exists in the human race . . . and that may be for a very long time to come if we meet, Out There, another species that is as mean, as nasty, and as highly competitive as we are.

But that is another story.　　　　　　　　　●

BIBLIOGRAPHY

The Lessons of History, Will and Ariel Durant, Simon and Schuster, New York, 1968

The Story of Man, Carleton S. Coon, Alfred A. Knopf, Inc., New York, 1962

"Strategic Areas In Space—The Panama Theory," Dandridge M. Cole, Institute of Aerospace Sciences, Los Angeles, March 15, 1962.

Interplanetary Flight, Arthur C. Clarke, Harper & Bros., New York, 1950.

The Moon Is A Harsh Mistress, Robert A. Heinlein, G. P. Putnam's Sons, New York, 1966.

The Third Industrial Revolution, G. Harry Stine, G. P. Putnam's Sons, New York, 1975, Revised Edition, Ace Books, New York, 1979.

Colony, Ben Bova, Simon & Schuster, New York, 1978.

Exploring The Secrets of Space, I. M. Levitt and Dandridge M. Cole, Prentice-Hall, Englewood Cliffs, New Jersey, 1963.

DOMINO DOMINE

by Dean Ing

And so on—*ad infinitum?*

Long before he saw signal fires through the great spyglass, Pontifex knew the taste of victory, and of fear. The new land-bridge—conceived in love from heaven, born in the fury of undersea tectonics—was a sword with two edges.

The Presence was no godlet of vague or paltry predictions: He had promised the landbridge, miraculously formed before the Infidel could garrison their coastal city. The steam carts of Pontifi-

cal legions had dashed across baking mudflates to capture the Infidel city in a single day. Soon that city would furnish youths for the Sacrifice of Innocents in accord with the pact between Pontifex and The Presence in the holy flame. Still, it was one thing to capture a city, quite another to hold it against the aroused Infidel.

If the invasion failed, soon the landbridge would be choked in ignominious retreat. The half-trained savages of Pontifical legions would be followed by sturdy yeoman Infidel farmers; one beachhead would go, then another; and soon, like game tiles toppling one against the next, the very redoubts of The Presence might fall. For most of the priesthood, failure of the holy war was unthinkable. For the high priest it was all too thinkable. For, if Pontifex was first among the devout, he was also prone to question. It was a burden he shared with none but The Presence.

Pontifex blinked as he turned away from the eyepiece, caught the eye of his aide. "Flash the message, Delain," he said; "the Infidel city is ours."

Delain, militarily correct, let relief show in his tanned features as he bowed himself out of the observatory. Pontifex often wondered at the wisdom of using a brigade colonel as he used Delain. Yet Delain knew his place, and that of every man in the Pontifical forces. If a signal mirror or a guard or a weapon failed, Delain saw to the replacement without asking instructions. It was a virture uncommon on this side of the narrow sea, Pontifex thought with chagrin. Unquestioning fidelity to The Presence caused a dependence in men's minds. *It embrittles the soul*, he thought, and quickly diverted himself from this heresy.

Domino Domine

The heliograph was already flashing the news to his own city, far below the mountain heights. Before Pontifex could descend his funicular railway to the temple, the message would be shouted to every hovel, would be filtering toward the hill tribesmen and the laboring peasants. And the clattering sulphurous funicular would give Pontifex time to compose himself for audience with The Presence.

The old priest found Delain staring across mudflats toward a twinkling on the horizon. "Some genius with our assault battalions already has his flasher in use, your grace," said Delain, surprised as always at efficiency in the ranks. "Shall I stay here and decode?"

"I shall need you to make ready for the solemn rite," Pontifex replied. "Surely the innocents will be rushed back immediately."

"Even before our wounded, wire," said Delain, his tone making no secret of his disapproval. "Need you rush? We can hardly spare the oil for a mass sacrifice now, of all times." The priest said nothing as he settled his slender old body in a funicular seat; his stare was reproof enough. Delain gnawed his lip. "And I am not a priest, but a fool to meddle in priestly matters," he said, bowing low. The faintest suggestion of a smile tugged at the mouth of Pontifex. Delain saw forgiveness and took a calculated risk. "Or has The Presence revealed how to double our reserves of oil?"

Pontifex engaged the lever that would begin their descent. Always alert, Delain had pinpointed the problem. If they were to proceed with transport of vital troops, it must be within days. The steam carts would need all of their available processed oil and much of the wood. Yet the mass sacrifice would use half of the hoarded fuel.

"Be tranquil, Delain," said the old priest over the railway's clacking; "I can only say that the bargain has been struck. The Presence will provide."

Delain sighed unhappily. "I must accept what I fail to understand. It takes many precious barrels of oil to incinerate a thousand children."

Pontifex frowned. He was thinking the same thing.

The innermost temple portal dilated at the voice of Pontifex, who had long ago ceased to wonder at such minor miracles in the sanctum. Soon, replenishing aromatic oil in the crystal flameholder, he had rekindled the holy flame and, in time, was rewarded.

"Rise, Pontifex," said the familiar voice, its gentle thunder thrilling with vibrato. Filling the flame was, literally, the Godhead; and the face of The Presence was beautiful. Wise brown eyes gazed below tight black ringlets. The full beard surrounded a mouth that some might call faintly sensuous, and the mouth was smiling. The face of The Presence could be as cold as ocean depths but on this day it was warm and loving. The flame danced and shuddered as the voice issued from it. "You may speak."

"Victory, Lord," replied the priest. "Our steam carts will return within a day's time, laden with captives. The day after, we will perform the rite."

"Then smile, Pontifex. I am pleased." Yet something in the voice was less than pleased.

Pontifex tried to smile. "I—my aides are troubled, Lord. The problem may be trivial, but the sacrifice will consume most of our oil reserves. Am I presumptuous?"

"Yes; but you tremble in your presumption. I am not threatened, Pontifex." Then, more sternly: "Not by mortal impudence, in any event. I shall provide."

"Thank you, Lord. Where will we find the oil?"

"You will continue to extract it as always."

"Lord, we proceed at full capacity. Without more oil, we would allow the Infidel time to mobilize and overrun our positions. If our troops lose heart they will panic. And presently, Infidel farmers might sweep into this very sanctum with my blood on their boots."

"Unless diverted by a locust plague in their fields," said The Presence.

Pontifex considered this. "And if they elect to abandon their fields to the insects?"

The face hardened. "The sea bottom shook once to raise your landbridge," it reminded. "Am I impotent to sink it again?"

Pontifex dropped his eyes. "Infinitely potent, Lord. You would do all this?" He did not dare—or need—to ask the fate of the assault battalions in such an event.

"I shall do what I shall do. Two days hence, the mouth of the infinite will attend your mass sacrifice."

Pontifex let his delight show. "May I call the faithful to the temple as witnesses?"

After the briefest pause: "Even the heavens grow uncertain—but by all means, call the faithful if you like. And now make haste, Pontifex; do not tarry with your women."

The priest sensed, as he had a few times before

a wry amusement in The Presence. He smiled back as the flame dimmed. its Godhead fading. "My Lord is jealous with my time," he said amiably.

And from the dying flame: "All gods are jealous, Pontifex."

The suggestion of many gods was a heresy so profound that Pontifex took it for a divine jest. The priest hurried to the portal, his confidence rekindled. Perhaps Delain could oversee a massive stockpiling of wood for the steam carts. With piles of wood at waystations along the mudflats? Perhaps. Such questions were below the notice of a god. *All gods*, his mind whispered.

Old Pontifex stood in bright sunlight before the temple facing the vast stone bowl between himself and the faithful throng of the city. He did not permit himself the luxury of a frown as he saw a guard hurl one of the captive children into the

depression. Even though the children had been drugged during meals, they would feel some pain.

And Pontifex was not a cruel man. Far better, he felt, if the children went peacefully into the shallow lake of oil. From his vantage point he saw the piles of wood that already began to dot the horizon. Delain had insisted that only by a miracle would the waystations be sufficient—and Pontifex had agreed with a secret smile.

By now, more than half of the children had slid into the huge oil-filled depression. Most of the city's people were gathered below to witness the ancient holy rite. Or more correctly, they had gathered to behold the mouth of the infinite, the enormous cyclonic void that would form above the blazing pool to swallow the sacrificial smoke.

Once, the people across the shallow sea had made similar sacrifices until some herbalist fool had found means to control the birthrate. It was only a matter of time before this technology became a religious issue, then an enmity; and now the Infidel refused to sacrifice their surplus youth since, they claimed, there was no surplus. This final refusal had provoked the eternal, all-wise Presence. For as far back as records existed, sacrificial rites had always been demanded by The Presence. What right-minded person could deny a deity who so willingly demonstrated His existence?

Pontifex regretted the need to give youthful lives but, in his regret, stepped forward with his torch. The last of the captives stumbled forward into the pool.

And then, incredibly, a group of half-grown children scrambled from the pool, oil glistening on their naked bodies. The had waited for the approach of the high priest and now flew into an organized pattern of action that suggested careful training. Twoscore of the youngsters fell on the guards, while a similar number sprinted toward Pontifex.

Obviously, the group had refused their drugged food. They had been taught what to expect, could plan independently, were fired with a desperate valor unknown to the ignorant legions they defied. Pontifex stood his ground on leaden feet, unwilling to show his fear. A detached segment of his mind marveled at the display and wondered if Delain were napping behind him.

Delain's response was a barked command. The heavy whistle of thrown spears passed over Pontifex into the onrushing children. Delain led the countercharge, hacking with his shortsword, fending off the pummeling empty hands. Only a lad and a girl, both near puberty, escaped. Oblivious to the screams behind them they drew nearer, until a flung shortsword pierced the boy's side. He fell, sliding in blood and oil, yet the girl did not falter.

Pontifex hurled the torch. The girl staggered, fell to one knee, and in that instant her body was sheathed in flame as the oil on her body ignited. She stood again, faced the priest as he folded his arms in a crucial show of disdain. Through the flames she stared at Pontifex; and in her face he saw a terrible resolve. She managed to reach him, clasped him in fiery embrace.

Pontifex held his breath, slid from his crimson robe as the girl reeled gasping. When she fell, she did not rise again, and Pontifex paused only to recover the torch before striding to the lip of the sacrificial pool. Though unharmed he was too shaken to pronounce the invocation, but all the city's multitudes applauded as he let the torch roll into the oil below.

The roar of the pyre found its match from a hundred thousand throats; invoking The Presence, drowning bleated cries from inside the smoky inferno. Delain took his position behind the priest, the guards scrambling back from the heat while Pontifex, ritually proper though half unclothed, backed away pace by stately pace.

From Delain, behind him: "The fault was mine, sire."

"Nonesense. Who could expect such resolution from captive children?"

"I could, sire."

"Yes, perhaps you could. A great pity."

"A great waste."

High above them, the mouth of the infinite swirled into being. Roiling greasy smoke arose slowly at first, then thrust itself curling into the vortex that wailed overhead, an enormous invisible maw sucking the sacrificial smoke into nowhere. There were no more cries from the victims, no more hails from the crowd; only the steady cyclonic howl from above. It could not happen, yet it always happened. Therefore it was miraculous, an awesome demonstration of the power of The Presence. Through many tomorrows, thought Pontifex, the devout might fight more faithfully now..

They would need to. As individuals, the Infidel made the superior fighter. Was The Presence, then, a lord of inferiors? This thought would not subside, and Pontifex knew that its open expression would destroy him.

Gazing aloft, the old priest feared that The Presence had read his thoughts, for the huge mouth flickered from existence, reappeared, wafted from view again. The charnel stench of human sacrifice spread as the smoke continued to rise from the pool of fire. Presently it drifted, a horrifying omen, over the city and its frightened people. Never before had The Presence rejected such a sacrifice.

Pontifex tended the holy flame with trembling fingers, trying to ignore the sensation of ice that lay in his vitals. For a time the flame danced by itself over the carven crystal, uninhabited. At last, when fear overhung Pontifex as the smoke pall overhung his city, there was a swirling in the flame. It bade him speak.

"Lord," he croaked, and faltered. "Lord," he tried again, failed again. Ignoring arthritic pain, the priest abased himself on the cold flagstones. Muffled: "I failed you, Lord."

"No, Pontifex. You have served well."

"But—you refused the Sacrifice of Innocents?" The priest rested on his knees, tears streaking the lined old face.

Something in the hallowed features seemed awry. If a god could register perplexity, it might be registered thus. "The failure was not yours, Pontifex." A wisp of smile. "I was—distracted." It seemed that more was to be said, and then it seemed that The Presence had thought better of it.

"The people call it the worst of omens, Lord. Their fear spreads to the provinces. My aide reports flasher messages from across the landbridge.

Our gains are imperiled, though there is hope." He attempted a summation; could only add, "All is not well here."

"Nor in the heavens. Has it occurred to you that your aide fears to tell you the worst?"

"It has, Lord. Delain fears me too much. In some ways it might be better if I did not pretend to godlike knowledge."

There was a long silence, as the face in the flame studied the troubled priest. Then: "Sufficient knowledge equals divinity?"

"I did not suggest that, Lord."

"No; I did. Pontifex, if you took Delain into your confidence, explained your miraculous wisdom, would he be the better for it?"

Pontifex wondered how he sould reply and decided upon total candor. "For himself, probably yes. For my purpose—which is to serve you, Lord—certainly no. Did I answer wisely?"

Something between a chuckle and a sigh. "I hope so. You have served me as your Delain has served you. Even while hating the bloody work I gave you."

"You saw my thoughts, Lord."

"I saw your face, Pontifex."

"The Presence is all-seeing," the priest murmured.

Quickly: "And what if I were not? Is it possible to forgive a god that fails?"

Pontifex felt the tears drying cold on his cheeks, overwhelmed by the deeper cold in his belly. "Lord: a god cannot be a god, and fail."

"True." Softly, with a note almost of pleading: "And I foresee that I must fail you."

'Pontifex, misunderstanding, cried out. "What

have we done to deserve your forsaking us?"

"Nothing. The universe takes little note of the deserving poor. Let me reward your devotion with truth: I can no longer maintain the energy source that permits me to interfere with your natural events. I might be an observer; nothing more. Seismic disturbance, plague, even the mass transfer locus you call the mouth of the infinite. All will be lost to me, therefore to you."

Pontifex cast his mind ahead to guess at a future without divine guidance. "The people believe in me, Lord."

"As you believed in me, Pontifex. *As we believed in our gods,*" the voice thundered in savage irony. *"As our gods did in theirs!"*

Pontifex clasped his head between his palms to keep it from bursting. "It is painful to hold such thoughts," he muttered. "Why must you abandon us?"

"Our gods tell us that *their* gods are losing a great war," was the reply. "When we lose assistance from above, those below us must suffer the same fate. Perhaps the universe grows tired of gods."

"Or of wars in their names," the priest said bitterly. "What use did you make of the ghastly sacrifices we perpetuated in your honor?"

The flame steadied as the voice fell silent. When it spoke again, it spoke with reluctance. "A flavoring, Pontifex. A condiment highly regarded by my civilization."

The priest stood erect. "Spice," he whispered. "Can you have been victimized as badly by your own gods?"

"Considering the holy war we seem fated to lose

on several worlds? Oh, yes. Yes, we think so. There may be a spark of the savage in all beings, Pontifex. We defaced our temples. Are you civilized enough to forgive?"

"Were you?" With agility that surprised him, Pontifex smashed the crystal flameholder. Small pools of oil spread across the altar and over the stones, feeding blazes that flickered toward ancient draperies.

As the sanctum began to burn, the old priest shed his robes. The portal dilated for the last time, and staring back, Pontifex saw in each flame the same once-beloved face. In unison, the images called to him. "Absolution, Pontifex," they pleaded.

To no avail. Many generations would pass, the burned temple a long-forgotten ruin, before hearth-fires on the peaceful world of Pontifex were entirely free of the voice that begged from the flames. ●

ANTINOMY

They were a
perfect match,
and then
he changed...

BY SPIDER ROBINSON

The first awakening was just awful.

She was naked and terribly cold. She appeared to be in a plastic coffin, from whose walls grew wrinkled plastic arms with plastic hands that did things to her. Most of the things hurt dreadfully. *But I don't have nightmares like this*, she thought wildly. She tried to say it aloud, and it came out, "A."

Even allowing for the sound-deadening coffin walls, the voice sounded distant. "Christ, she's awake already."

Eyes appeared over hers, through a transparent panel she had failed to see since it had showed only a ceiling the same color as the coffin's interior. The face was masked and capped in white, the eyes pouched in wrinkles. *Marcus Welby. Now it makes enough sense. Now I'll believe it. I don't have nightmares like this.*

"I believe you're right." The voice was professionally detached. A plastic hand selected something that lay by her side, pressed it to her arm. "There."

Thank you, Doctor. If my brain doesn't want to remember what you're operating on me for, I don't much suppose it'll want to record the operation itself. Bye.

She slept.

The second awakening was better.

She was astonished not to hurt. She had expected to hurt, somewhere, although she had also expected to be too dopey to pay it any mind. Neither condition obtained.

She was definitely in a hospital, although some

of the gadgetry seemed absurdly ultramodern. *This certainly isn't Bellevue*, she mused. *I must have contracted something fancy. How long has it been since I went to bed "last night"?*

Her hands were folded across her belly; her right hand held something hard. It turned out to be a traditional nurse-call buzzer — save that it was cordless. Lifting her arm to examine it had told her how terribly weak she was, but she thumbed the button easily — it was not spring-loaded. "*Nice* hospital," she said aloud, and her voice sounded too high. *Something with my throat? Or my ears? Or my . . . brain?*

The buzzer might be improved, but the other end of the process had not changed appreciably; no one appeared for a while. She awarded her attention to the window beside her, no contest in a hospital room, and what she saw through it startled her profoundly.

She *was* in Bellevue, after all, rather high up in the new tower: the rooftops below her across the street and the river beyond them told her that. But she absorbed the datum almost unconsciously, much more startled by the policeman who was flying above those rooftops, a few hundred feet away, in an oversize garbage can.

Yep, my brain. The operation was a failure, but the patient lived.

For a ghastly moment there was great abyss within her, into which she must surely fall. But her mind had more strength than her body. She willed the abyss to disappear, and it did. *I may be insane, but I'm not going to go nuts over it*, she thought, and giggled. She decided the giggle was a healthy sign, and did it again, realizing her error when she found she could not stop.

It was mercifully shorter than such episodes usually are; she simply lost the strength to giggle. The room swam for a while, then, but lucidity returned rather rapidly.

Let's see. Time travel, huh? That means . . .

The door opened to admit — not a nurse — but a young man of about twenty-five, five years her junior. He was tall and somehow self-effacing. His clothes and appearance did not strike her as conservative, but she decided they probably were — for this era. He did not look like a man who would preen more than convention required.

"What year is this, anyway?" she asked as he opened his mouth, and he closed it. He began to look elated and opened his mouth again, and she said "And what did I die of?" and he closed it again. He was silent then for a moment, and when he had worked it out she could see that the elation was gone.

But in its place was a subtler, more personal pleasure. "I congratulate you on the speed of your uptake," he said pleasantly. "You've just saved me most of twenty minutes of hard work."

"The hell you say. I can deduce what *happened*, all right, but that saves you twenty seconds, max. 'How' and 'why' are going to take just as long as you expected. And don't forget 'when'." Her voice still seemed too high, though less so.

"How about 'who'? I'm Bill McLaughlin"

"I'm Marie Antoinette, *what the hell year is it?*" The italics cost her the last of her energy: as he replied "1990," his voice faded and the phosphor dots of her vision began to enlarge and drift apart. She was too bemused by his answer to be annoyed.

Something happened to her arm again, and picture and sound returned with even greater clarity. "Forgive me, Ms. Harding. The first thing I'm supposed to do is give you the stimulant. But then the first thing you're supposed to do is be semiconscious."

"And we've dispensed with the second thing," she said, her voice normal again now, "which is telling me that I've been a corpsicle for ten years. So tell me why, and why I don't *remember* any of it. As far as I know I went to sleep last night and woke up here, with a brief interlude inside something that must have been a defroster."

"I thought you *had* remembered, from your first question. I hoped you had, Ms. Harding. You'd have been the first . . . never mind — your next question made it plain that you don't. Very briefly, ten years ago you discovered that you had leukemia . . ."

"Myelocytic or lymphocytic?"

"Neither. Acute."

She paled. "No wonder I've suppressed the memory."

"You haven't. Let me finish. Acute Luke was the diagnosis, a new rogue variant with a bitch's bastard of a prognosis. In a little under sixteen weeks they tried corticosteroids, L-aspiraginase, cytosine arabinoside, massive irradiation, and mercrystate crystals, with no more success than they'd expected, which was none and negatory. They told you that the new bone-marrow transplant idea showed great promise, but it might be a few years. And so you elected to become a corpsicle. You took another few weeks arranging your affairs, and then went to a Cold Sleep Center and had yourself frozen."

"Alive?"

"They had just announced the big breakthrough. A week of drugs and a high-helium atmosphere and you can defrost a living person instead of preserved meat. You got in on the ground floor."

"And the catch?"

"The process scrubs the top six <u>months</u> to a year off your memory."

"Why?"

"I've been throwing around terminology to demonstrate how thoroughly I've read your file. But I'm not a doctor. I don't understand the alleged 'explanation' they gave me, and I dare say you won't either."

"Okay." She forgot the matter, instantly and forever. "If you're not a doctor, who are you, Mr. McLaughlin?"

"Bill. I'm an Orientator. The phrase won't be familiar to you —"

" — but I can figure it out, Bill. Unless things have slowed down considerably since I was alive, ten years is a hell of a jump. You're going to teach me how to dress and speak and recognize the ladies' room."

"And hopefully to stay alive."

"For how long? Did they fix it?"

"Yes. A spinal implant, right after you were thawed. It releases a white-cell antagonist into your bloodstream, and it's triggered by a white-cell surplus. The antagonist favors rogue cells."

"Slick. I always liked feedback control. Is it foolproof?"

"Is anything? Oh, you'll need a new implant every five years, and you'll have to take a week of chemotherapy here to make sure the implant isn't rejected before we can let you go. But the worst side-effect we know of is partial hair-loss. You're fixed, Ms. Harding."

She relaxed all over, for the first time since the start of the conversation. With the relaxation came a dreamy feeling, and she knew she had been subtly drugged, and was pleased that she had resisted it, quite unconsciously, for as long as had been necessary. She disliked don't-worry drugs; she preferred to worry if she had a mind to.

"Virginia. Not Ms. Harding. And I'm pleased with the Orientator I drew, Bill. It takes you a while to get to the nut, but you haven't said a single inane thing yet, which under the circumstances makes you a remarkable person."

"I like to think so, Virginia. By the way, you'll doubtless be pleased to know that your fortune has come through the last ten years intact. In fact, it's actually grown considerably."

"There goes your no-hitter."

"Beg pardon?"

"Two stupid statements in one breath. First, of *course* my fortune has grown. A fortune the size of mine can't *help* but grow — which is one of the major faults of our economic system. What could be sillier than a goose that insists on burying you in golden eggs? Which leads to number two: I'm anything but pleased. I was hoping against hope that I was broke."

His face worked briefly, ending in a puzzled frown. "You're probably right on the first count, but I think the second is ignorance rather than stupidity. I've never been rich." His tone was almost wistful.

"Count your blessings. And be grateful you can count that high."

He looked dubious. "I suppose I'll have to take your word for it."

"When do I start getting hungry?"

"Tomorrow. You can walk now, if you don't overdo it, and in about an hour you'll be required to sleep."

"Well, let's go."

"Where to?"

"Eh? *Outside*, Bill. Or the nearest balcony or solarium. I haven't had a breath of fresh air in ten years."

"The solarium it is."

As he was helping her into a robe and slippers the door chimed and opened again, admitting a man in the time-honored white garb of a medical man on duty, save that the stethoscope around his neck was as cordless as the call-buzzer had been. The pickup was doubtless in his breast pocket, and she was willing to bet that it was warm to the skin.

The newcomer appeared to be a few years older than she, a pleasant-looking man with gray-ribbed temples and plain features. She recognized the wrinkled eyes and knew he was the doctor who had peered into her plastic coffin.

McLaughlin said, "Hello, Dr. Higgins. Virginia Harding, Dr. Thomas Higgins, Bellevue's Director of Cryonics."

Higgins met her eyes squarely and bowed. "Ms. Harding. I'm pleased to see you up and about."

Still has the same detached voice. Stuffy man. "You did a good job on me, Dr. Higgins."

"Except for a moment of premature consciousness, yes, I did. But the machines say you weren't harmed psychologically, and I'm inclined to believe them."

"They're right. I'm some tough."

"I know. That's why I brought you up to Level One Awareness in a half-day instead of a week. I knew your subconscious would fret less."

Discriminating machines, she thought. *I don't know that I like that.*

"Doctor," McLaughlin cut in, "I hate to cut you off, but Ms. Harding has asked for fresh air, and — "

" — and has less than an hour of consciousness left today. I understand. Don't let me keep you."

"Thank you, Doctor," Virginia Harding said. "I'd like to speak further with you tomorrow, if you're free."

He almost frowned, caught himself. "Later in the week, perhaps. Enjoy your walk."

"I shall. Oh, how I shall. Thank you again."

"Thank Hoskins and Parvati. They did the implant."

"I will, tomorrow. Good-bye, Doctor."

She left with McLaughlin, and as soon as the door had closed behind them, Higgins went to the window and slammed his fist into it squarely, shattering the shatterproof glass and two knuckles. Shards dropped eighty long stories, and he did not hear them land.

McLaughlin entered the office and closed the door.

Higgins's office was not spare or austere. The furnishings were many and comfortable, and in fact the entire room had a lived-in air which hinted that Higgins's apartment might well be spare and austere. Shelves of books covered two walls; most looked medical and all looked used. The predominant color of the room was black — not at all a fashionable color — but in no single instance was the black morbid, any more than is the night sky. It gave a special vividness to the flowers on the desk, which were the red of rubies, and to the profusion of hand-tended plants which sat beneath the broad east window (now opaqued in a riotous splash of many colors for which our language has only the single word "green." It put crisper outlines on anything that moved in the office, brought both visitors and owner into sharper relief.

But the owner was not making use of this sharpening of perception at the moment. He was staring fixedly down at his desk; precisely, in fact, at the empty place where a man will put a picture of his wife and family if he has them. He could not have seen McLaughlin if he tried; his eyes were blinded with tears. Had McLaughlin not seen them, he might have thought the other to be in an autohypnotic trance or a warm creative fog, neither of which states were unusual enough to

call for comment.

Since he did, he did not back silently out of the office. "Tom." There was no response. "Tom," he said again, a little louder, and then "TOM!"

"Yes?" Higgins said evenly, sounding like a man talking on an intercom. His gaze remained fixed, but the deep-set wrinkles around it relaxed a bit.

"She's asleep."

Higgins nodded. He took a bottle from an open drawer and swallowed long. He didn't have to uncap it first, and there weren't many swallows that size left. He set it, clumsily, on the desk.

"For God's sake, Tom," McLaughlin said half-angrily. "You remind me of Monsieur Rick in *Casablanca*. Want me to play 'As Time Goes By' now?"

Higgins looked up for the first time, and smiled beatifically. "You might," he said, voice steady. " 'You *must* remember this . . . as time goes by.' " He smiled again. "I often wonder." He looked down again, obviously forgetting McLaughlin's existence.

Self-pity in this man shocked McLaughlin, and cheerful self-pity disturbed him profoundly. "Jesus," he said harshly. "That bad?" Higgins did not hear. He saw Higgins's hand then, with its half-glove of bandage, and sucked air through his teeth. He called Higgins's name again, elicited no reaction at all.

He sighed, drew his gun and put a slug into the ceiling. The roar filled the office, trapped by soundproofing. Higgins started violently, becoming fully aware just as his own gun cleared the holster. He seemed quite sober.

"Now that I've got your attention," McLaughlin said dryly, "would you care to tell me about it?"

"No." Higgins grimaced. "Yes and no. I don't suppose I have much choice. She didn't remember a thing." His voice changed for the last sentence; it was very nearly a question.

"No, she didn't."

"None of them have yet. Almost a hundred awakenings, and not one remembers anything that happened more than ten to twelve months before they were put to sleep. And still somehow I hoped . . . I had hope . . ."

McLaughlin's voice was firm. "When you gave me her file, you said you 'used to know her,' and that you didn't want to go near her 'to avoid upsetting her.' You asked me to give her special attention, to take the best possible care of her, and you threw in some flattery about me being your best Orientator. Then you come barging into her room on no pretext at all, chat aimlessly, break your hand and get drunk. So you loved her. And you loved her in her last year."

"I diagnosed her leukemia," Higgins said emotionlessly. "It's hard to miss upper abdomen swelling and lymph node swelling in the groin when you're making love, but I managed for weeks. It was after she had the tooth pulled and it wouldn't stop bleeding that . . ." He trailed off.

"She loved you too."

"Yes." Higgins's voice was bleak, hollow.

"Bleeding Christ, Tom," McLaughlin burst out. "Couldn't you have waited to . . ." He broke off, thinking bitterly that Virginia Harding had given him too much credit.

"We tried to. We knew that every day we waited decreased her chances of surviving cryology, but we tried. She insisted that we try. Then the crisis came . . . oh damn it, Bill, *damn* it."

McLaughlin was glad to hear the profanity — it was the first sign of steam blowing off. "Well, she's alive and healthy now."

"Yes. I've been thanking God for that for three months now, ever since Hoskins and Parvati announced the unequivocal success of spinal implants. I've thanked God over ten thousand times, and I don't think He believed me once. I don't think *I* believed me once. Now doesn't that make me a selfish son of a bitch?"

McLaughlin grinned. "Head of Department and you live like a monk, because you're selfish. For years, every dime you make disappears down a hole somewhere, and everybody wonders why you're so friendly with Hoskins & Parvati, who aren't even in your own *department*, and only now, as I'm figuring out where the money's been going, do I realize what a truly selfish son of a bitch you are, Higgins."

Higgins smiled horribly. "We talked about it a lot, that last month. I wanted to be frozen too, for as long as they had to freeze her."

"What would that have accomplished? Then neither of you would have remembered."

"But we'd have entered and left freeze at the *same time*, and come out of it with sets of memories that ran nearly to the day we met. We'd effectively be precisely the people who fell in love once before; we could have left notes for ourselves and the rest would've been inevitable. But she wouldn't hear of it. She pointed out that the period in question could be any fraction of forever, with no warranty. I insisted, and got quite histrionic about it. Finally she brought up our age difference."

"I wondered about the chronology."

"She was thirty, I was twenty-five. Your age. It was something we kidded about, but it stung a bit when we did. So she asked me to wait five years, and then if I still wanted to be frozen, fine. In those five years I clawed my way up to head of section here, because I wanted to do everything I could to ensure her survival. And in the fifth year they thought her type of leukemia might be curable with marrow transplants, so I hung around for the two years it took to be sure they were wrong. And in the eighth year Hoskins started looking for a safe white-cell antagonist, and again I had to stay room temperature to finance him, because nobody else could smell that he was a genius. When he met Parvati, I knew they'd lick it, and I told myself that if they needed me, that meant she needed me. I wasn't wealthy like her — I had to keep working to keep them both funded properly. So I stayed."

Higgins rubbed his eyes, then made his hands lie very still before him, left on right. "Now there's a ten year span between us, the more pronounced because she hasn't experienced a single minute of it. Will she love me again or won't she? " The bandaged right hand escaped from the left, began to tap on the desk. "For ten years I told myself I could stand to know the answer to that question. For ten years it was the last thing I thought before I fell asleep and the first thing I thought when I woke up. *Will she love me or won't she?*

"She made me promise that I'd tell her everything when she was awakened, that I'd tell her how our love had been. She swore that she'd love me again. I promised, and she must have known I lied, or suspected it, because she left a ten page letter to herself in her file. The day I became Department Head I burned the fucking thing. I don't want her to love me because she thinks she should.

"Will she love me or won't she? For ten years I believed I could face the answer. Then it came time to wake her up, and I lost my nerve. I couldn't stand to know the answer. I gave her file to you.

"And then I saw her on the monitor, heard her voice coming out of my desk, and I knew I couldn't stand *not* to know."

He reached clumsily for the bottle, and knocked it clear off the desk. Incredibly, it contrived to shatter on the thick black carpet, staining it a deeper black. He considered this, while the autovac cleaned up the glass, clacking in disapproval.

"Do you know a liquor store that delivers?"

"In *this* day and age?" McLaughlin exclaimed, but Higgins was not listening. "Jesus Christ," he said suddenly. "Here." He produced a flask and passed it across the desk.

Higgins looked him in the eye. "Thanks, Bill." He drank.

McLaughlin took a long swallow himself and passed it back. They sat in silence for a while, in a communion and a comradeship as ancient as alcohol, as pain itself. Synthetic leather creaked convincingly as they passed the flask. Their breathing slowed.

If a clock whirs on a deskface and no one is listening, is there really a sound? In a soundproof office with opaqued windows, is it not always night? The two men shared the long night of the present, forsaking past and future, for nearly half an hour, while all around them hundreds upon hundreds worked, wept, smiled, dozed, watched television, screamed, were visited by relatives and friends, smoked, ate, died.

At last McLaughlin sighed and studied his hands. "When I was a grad student," he said to them, "I did a hitch on an Amerind reservation in New Mexico. Got friendly with an old man named Wanoma, face like a map of the desert. Grandfather-grandson relationship — close in that culture. He let me see his own grandfather's bones. He taught me how to pray. One night the son of a nephew, a boy he'd had hopes for, got alone-drunk and fell off a motorcycle. Broke his neck. I heard about it and went to see Wanoma that night. We sat under the moon — it was a harvest moon — and watched a fire until it was ashes. Just after the last coal went dark, Wanoma lifted his head and cried out in Zuni. He cried out, 'Ai-yah, my heart is full of sorrow.'"

McLaughlin glanced up at his boss and took a swallow. "You know, it's impossible for a white man to say those words and not sound silly. Or theatrical. It's a simple statement of a genuine universal, and there's no way for a white man to say it. I've tried two or three times since. You can't say it in English."

Higgins smiled painfully and nodded.

"I cried out too," McLaughlin went on, "after Wanoma did. The English of it was, 'Ai-yah, my brother's heart is full of sorrow. His heart is my heart.' Happens I haven't ever tried to say that since, but you can see it sounds hokey too."

Higgins's smile became less pained, and his eyes lost some of their squint. "Thanks, Bill."

"What'll you do?"

The smile remained. "Whatever I must. I believe I'll take the tour with you day after tomorrow. You can use the extra gun."

The Orientator went poker-faced. "Are you up to it, Tom? You've got to be fair to her, you know."

"I know. Today's world is pretty crazy. She's got a right to integrate herself back into it without tripping over past karma. She'll never know. I'll have control on Thursday, Bill. Partly thanks to you. But you do know why I selected you for her Orientator, don't you?"

"No. I don't think I do."

"I thought you'd at least have suspected. Personality Profiles are a delightful magic. Perhaps if we ever develop a science of psychology we'll understand why we get results out of them. According to the computer, your PP matches almost precisely my own — of ten years ago. Probably why we get along so well."

"I don't follow."

"Is love a matter of happy accident or a matter of psychological inevitability? Was what 'Ginia and I had fated in the stars, or was it a chance jigsawing of personality traits? Will the woman she was ten years ago love the man I've become? Or the kind of man I was then? Or some third kind? "

"Oh fine," McLaughlin said, getting angry. "So I'm your competition."

"Aha," Higgins pounced. "You do feel something for her."

"I . . ." McLaughlin got red.

"You're my competition," Higgins said steadily. "And, as you have said, you are my brother. Would you like another drink? "

McLaughlin opened his mouth, then closed it. He rose and left in great haste, and when he had gained the hallway he cannoned into a young nurse with red hair and improbably gray eyes. He mumbled apology and continued on his way, failing to notice her. He did not know Deborah Manning.

Behind him, Higgins passed out.

Throughout the intervening next day Higgins was conscious of eyes on him. He was conscious of little enough else as he sleepwalked through his duties. The immense hospital complex seemed to have been packed full of gray jello, very near to setting. He plowed doggedly through it, making noises with his mouth, making decisions, making marks on pieces of paper, discharging his responsibilities with the least part of his mind. But he was conscious of the eyes.

A hospital grapevine is like no other on earth. If you want a message heard by every employee, it is quicker to tell two nurses and an intern than it would be to assemble the staff and make an announcement. Certainly McLaughlin had said nothing, even to his hypothetical closest friend; he

knew that any closest friend has at least one *other* closest friend. But at least three OR personnel knew that the Old Man had wakened one personally the other day. And a janitor knew that the Old Man was in the habit of dropping by the vaults once a week or so, just after the start of the graveyard shift, to check on the nonexistent progress of a corpsicle named Harding. And the OR team and the janitor worked within the same (admittedly huge) wing, albeit on different floors. So did the clerk-typist in whose purview were Virginia Harding's files, and she was engaged to the anesthetist. Within twenty-four hours, the entire hospital staff and a majority of the patients had added two and two.

(Virginia Harding, of course, heard nary a word, got not so much as a hint. A hospital staff may spill Mercurochrome. It often spills blood. But it never spills beans.)

Eyes watched Higgins all day. And so perhaps it was natural that eyes watched him in his dreams that night. But they did not make him afraid or uneasy. Eyes that watch oneself continuously become, after a time, like a second ego, freeing the first from the burden of introspection. They almost comforted him. They helped.

I have been many places, touched many lives since I touched hers, he thought as he shaved the next morning, *and been changed by them. Will she love me or won't she?*

There were an endless three more hours of work to be taken care of that morning, and then at last the jello dispersed, his vision cleared and she was before him, dressed for the street, chatting with McLaughlin. There were greetings, explanations of some sort were made for his presence in the party, and they left the room, to solve the mouse's maze of corridors that led to the street and the city outside.

It was a warm fall day. The streets were unusually crowded, with people and cars, but he knew they would not seem so to Virginia. The sky seemed unusually overcast, the air particularly muggy, but he knew it would seem otherwise to her. The faces of the pedestrians they passed seemed to him markedly cheerful and optimistic, and he felt that this was a judgment with which she *would* agree. This was not a new pattern of thought for him. For over five years now, since the world she knew had changed enough for him to perceive, he had been accustomed to observe that world in the light of what she would think of it. Having an unconscious standard of comparison, he had marked the changes of the last decade more acutely than his contemporaries, more acutely perhaps than even McLaughlin, whose interest was only professional.

Too, knowing her better than McLaughlin, he was better able to anticipate the questions she would ask. A policeman went overhead in a floater bucket, and McLaughlin began to describe the effects that force-fields were beginning to exert on her transportation holdings and other financial interests. Higgins cut him off before she could, and described the effects single-person flight was having on social and sexual customs, winning a smile from her and a thoughtful look from the Orientator. When McLaughlin began listing some of the unfamiliar gadgetry she could expect to see, Higgins interrupted with a brief sketch of the current state of America's spiritual renaissance. When McLaughlin gave her a personal wrist-phone, Higgins showed her how to set it to refuse calls.

McLaughlin had, of course, already told her a good deal about Civil War Two and the virtual annihilation of the American black, and had been surprised at how little surprised she was. But when, now, he made a passing reference to the unparalleled savagery of the conflict, Higgins saw a chance to make points by partly explaining that bloodiness with a paraphrase of a speech Virginia herself had made ten years before, on the folly of an urban-renewal package concept which had sited low-income housing immediately around urban and suburban transportation hubs. "Built-in disaster," she agreed approvingly, and did not feel obliged to mention that the same thought had occurred to her a decade ago. Higgins permitted himself to be encouraged.

But about that time, as they were approaching one of the new downtown parks, Higgins noticed the expression on McLaughlin's face, and somehow recognized it as one he had seen before — from the inside.

At once he was ashamed of the fatuous pleasure he had been taking in outmaneuvering the younger man. It was a cheap triumph, achieved through unfair advantage. Higgins decided sourly that he would never have forced this "duel with his younger self" unless he had been just this smugly sure of the outcome, and his self-esteem dropped sharply. He shut his mouth, and resolved to let McLaughlin lead the conversation.

It immediately took a turning he could not have followed if he tried.

As the trio entered the park, they passed a group of teenagers. Higgins paid them no mind — he had long since reached the age when adolescents, especially in groups, regarded him as an alien life form, and he was nearly ready to agree with them. But he noticed Virginia Harding noticing them, and followed her gaze.

The group were talking in loud voices, the incomprehensible gibberish of the young. There was nothing Higgins could see about them that Harding ought to find striking. They were dressed no differently than any one of a hundred teenagers she had passed on the walk so far, were quite nondescript. Well, now that he looked closer, he saw rather higher-than-average intelligence in most of the faces. Honor-student types, down to the carefully-cultivated look of aged cynicism. That *was* rather at variance with the raucousness of their voices, but Higgins still failed to see what held Harding's interest.

"What on earth are they saying?" she asked, watching them over her shoulder as they passed.

Higgins strained, heard only nonsense. He saw McLaughlin grinning.

"They're Goofing," the Orientator said.

"Beg pardon?"

"Goofing. The very latest in sophisticated humor."

Harding still looked curious.

"It sort of grew out of the old Firesign Theater of the seventies. Their kind of comedy laid the groundwork for the immortal Spiwack, and he created Goofing, or as he called it, speaking with spooned tongue. It's a kind of double-talk, except that it's designed to actually convey information, more or less in spite of itself. The idea is to *almost* make sense, to get across as much of your point as possible without ever saying anything comprehensible."

Higgins snorted, afraid.

"I'm not sure I understand," Harding said.

"Well, for instance, if Spiwack wanted to publicly libel, say, the president, he'd Goof. Uh . . ." McLaughlin twisted his voice into a fair imitation of a broken-down prizefighter striving to sound authoritative. "That guy there, see, in my youth we would of referred to him as a man with a tissue-paper asshole. What you call a kinda guy what sucks blueberries through a straw, see? A guy like what would whistle at a doorknob, you know what I mean? He ain't got all his toes."

Harding began to giggle. Higgins began sweating, all over.

"I'm tellin' ya, the biggest plum *he*'s got is the one under his ear, see what I'm sayin'? If whiskers was pickles, he'd have a goat. First sign of saddlebags an' he'll be under his pants. If I was you I'd keep my finger out of *his* nose, an' you can forget I said so. Goodnight."

Harding was laughing out loud now. "That's marvelous!" A spasm shook her. "That's the most . . . *conspicuous* thing I've ever baked." McLaughlin began to laugh. "I've never been so identified in all my shoes." They were both laughing together now, and Higgins had about five seconds in which to grab his wrist-phone behind his back and dial his own code, before they could notice him standing there and realize they had left him behind and become politely apologetic, and he just made it, but even so he had time in which to reflect that a shared belly-laugh can be as intimate as making love. *It may even be a prerequisite*, he thought, and then his phone was humming its A-major chord.

The business of unclipping the earphone and fiddling with the gain gave him all the time he needed to devise an emergency that would require his return, and he marveled at his lightning cleverness, that balked at producing a joke. He really tried, as he spoke with his nonexistent caller, prolonging the conversation with grunts to give himself time. When he was ready he switched off, and in his best W.C. Fields voice said, "It appears that one of my clients has contracted farfalonis of the blowhole," and to his absolute horror they both said "Huh?" together and then got it, and in that moment he hated McLaughlin more than he had ever hated anything, even the cancer that had come sipping her blood a decade before. *Keep your face straight*, he commanded himself savagely. *She's looking at you.*

And McLaughlin rescued the moment, in that split second before Higgins's control would have cracked, doing his prizefighter imitation. "Aw Jeez, Tom, that's hard salami. If it ain't one thing, it's two things. Go ahead; we'll keep your shoes warm."

Higgins nodded. "Hello, Virginia."

"Gesundheit, Doctor," she said, regarding him oddly.

He turned on his heel to go, and saw the tallest of the group of teenagers fold at the waist, take four rapid steps backward and fall with the boneless sprawl of the totally drunk. *But drunks don't spurt red from their bellies*, Higgins thought dizzily, just as the flat *crack* reached his ears.

Mucker!

Eyes report: a middle-aged black man with three days' growth of beard, a hundred meters away and twenty meters up in a stolen floater bucket with blood on its surface. Firing a police rifle of extremely heavy caliber with snipersights. Clearly crazed with grief or stoned out of control, he is not making use of the sights, but firing from the hip. His forehead and cheek are bloody and one eye is

ruined: some policeman sold his floater dearly.

Memory reports: It has been sixteen weeks since the Treaty of Philadelphia officially "ended" C.W. II. Nevertheless, known-dead statistics are still filtering slowly back to next-of-kin; the envelope in his breast pocket looks like a government form letter.

Ears report: Two more shots have been fired. Despite eyes' report, his accuracy is hellish — each shot hit someone. Neither of them is Virginia.

Nose reports: All three (?) wounded have blown all sphincters. Death, too, has its own smell, as does blood. That other one: is that fear?

Hand reports: Gun located, clearing holster . . . now. Safety off, barrel coming up fast,

WHITE OUT!

The slug smashed into Higgins's side and spun him completely around twice before slamming him to earth beside the path. His brain continued to record all sensory reports, so in a sense he was conscious; but he would not audit these memories for days, so in a sense he was unconscious too. His head was placed so that he could see Virginia Harding, in a sideways crouch, extend her gun and fire with extreme care. McLaughlin stood tall before her, firing rapidly from the hip, and her shot took his right earlobe off. He screamed and dropped to one knee.

She ignored him and raced to Higgins's side. "It looks all right, Tom," she lied convincingly. She was efficiently taking his pulse as she fumbled with his clothing. "Get an ambulance," she barked at someone out of vision. Whoever it was apparently failed to understand the archaism, for she amended it to "A doctor, dammit. *Now*," and the whip of command was in her voice. As she turned back to Higgins, McLaughlin came up with a handkerchief pressed to his ear.

"You got him" he said weakly.

"I know," she said, and finished unbuttoning Higgins's shirt. Then, *"What the hell did you get in my way for?"*

"I . . . I," he stammered, taken aback, "I was trying to protect *you.*"

"From a rifle like *that?*" she blazed. "If you got between one of those slugs and me all you'd do is tumble it for me. Blasting away from the hip like a cowboy . . ."

"I was trying to spoil his aim," McLaughlin said stiffly.

"You bloody idiot, you can't scare a kamikaze! The only thing to do was drop him, fast."

"I'm sorry."

"I nearly blew your damn head off."

McLaughlin began an angry retort, but about then even Higgins's delayed action consciousness faded. The last sensation he retained was that of her hands gently touching his face. That made it a fine memory-sequence, all in all, and when he reviewed it later on he only regretted not having been there at the time.

All things considered, McLaughlin was rather lucky. It took him only three days of rather classical confusion to face his problem, conceive of several solutions, select the least drastic, and persuade a pretty nurse to help him put it into effect. But it was after they had gone to his apartment and gone to bed that he really got lucky: his penis flatly refused to erect.

He of course did not, at that time, think of this as a stroke of luck. He did not know Deborah Manning. He in fact literally did not know her last name. She had simply walked past at the right moment, a vaguely-remembered face framed in red hair, gray eyes improbable enough to stick in the mind. In a mood of go-to-hell desperation he had baldly propositioned her, as though this were still the promiscuous seventies, and he had been surprised when she accepted. He did not know Debbie Manning.

In normal circumstances he would have considered his disfunction trivial, done the gentlemanly thing and tried again in the morning. In the shape he was in it nearly cracked him. Even so, he tried to be chivalrous, but she pulled him up next to her with a gentle firmness and looked closely at him. He had the odd, inexplicable feeling that she had been . . . *prepared* for this eventuality.

He seldom watched peoples' eyes closely,—popular opinion and literary convention to the contrary, he found peoples' mouths much more expressive of the spirit within. But something about her eyes held his. Perhaps it was that they were not trying to. They were staring only for information, for a deeper understanding . . . he realized with a start that they were looking at his mouth. For a moment he started to *look* back, took in clean high cheeks and soft lips, was beginning to genuinely notice her for the first time when she said "Does she know?" with just the right mixture of tenderness and distance to open him up like a clam.

"No," he blurted, his pain once again demanding his attention.

"Well, you'll just have to tell her then," she said earnestly, and he began to cry.

"I can't," he sobbed, "I *can't*."

She took the word at face value. Her face saddened. She hugged him closer, and her shoulder blades were warm under his hands. "That *is* terrible. What is her name, and how did it come about?"

It no more occurred to him to question the ethics of telling her than it had occurred to him to wonder by what sorcery she had identified his brand of pain in the first place, or to wonder why she chose to involve herself in it. Head tucked in the hollow between her neck and shoulder, legs wrapped in hers, he told her everything in his heart. She spoke only to prompt him, keeping her *self* from his attention, and yet somehow what he told her held more honesty and truth than what he had been telling himself.

"He's been in the hospital for three days," he concluded, "and she's been to visit him twice a day — and she's begged off our Orientation Walks every damn day. She leaves word with the charge nurse."

"You've tried to see her anyway? After work?"

"No. I can read print."

"Can't you read the print on your own heart? You don't seem like a quitter to me, Bill."

"Dammit," he raged, "I don't *want* to love her. I've tried *not* to love her, and I can't get her out of my head."

She made the softest of snorting sounds. "You will be given a billion dollars if in the next ten seconds you do *not* think of a green horse." Pause. "You know better than that."

"Well, how do you get someone out of your head, then?"

"Why do you want to?"

"Why? Because . . ." he stumbled. "Well, this sounds silly in words, but . . . I haven't got the right to her. I mean, Tom has put literally his whole life into her for ten years now. He's not just my boss — he's my friend, and if he wants her that bad he ought to have her."

"She's an object, then? A prize? He shot more tin ducks, he wins her?"

"Of course not. I mean he ought to have his

chance with her, a fair chance, without tripping over the image of himself as a young stud. He's *earned* it. Dammit, I ... this sounds like ego, but I'm unfair competition. What man can compete with his younger self? "

"Any man who has grown as he aged," she said with certainty.

He pulled back — just far enough to be able to see her face. "What do you mean? " He sounded almost petulant.

She brushed hair from her face, freed some that was trapped between their bodies. "Why did Dr. Higgins rope you into this in the first place? "

He opened his mouth and nothing came out.

"He may not know," she said, "but his subconscious does. Yours does too, or you wouldn't be so damfool guilty."

"What are you talking about? "

"If you *are* unfair competition, he does not deserve her, and I don't care how many years he's dedicated to her sacred memory. Make up your mind: are you crying because you can't have her or because you could? " Her voice softened suddenly — took on a tone which only his subconscious associated with those of a father confessor from his Catholic youth. "Do you honestly believe in your heart of hearts that you could take her away from him if you tried? "

Those words could certainly have held sting, but they did not somehow. The silence stretched, and her face and gaze held a boundless compassion that told him that he must give her an answer, and that it must be the truth.

"I don't know," he cried, and began to scramble

from the bed. But her soft hands had a grip like iron — and there was nowhere for him to go. He sat on the side of the bed, and she moved to sit beside him. With the same phenomenal strength, she took his chin and turned his face to see hers. At the sight of it he was thunderstruck. Her face seemed to glow with a light of its own, to be somehow *larger* than it was, and with softer edges than flesh can have. Her neck muscles were bars of tension and her face and lips were utterly slack; her eyes were twin tractor beams of incredible strength locked on his soul, on his attention.

"Then you have to find out, don't you?" she said in the most natural voice in the world.

And she sat and watched his face go through several distinct changes, and after a time she said "Don't you?" again very softly.

"Tom is my friend," he whispered bleakly.

She released his eyes, got up and started getting dressed. He felt vaguely that he should stop her, but he could not assemble the volition. As she dressed, she spoke for the first time of herself. "All my life people have brought problems to me," she said distantly. "I don't know why. Sometimes I think I attract pain. They tell me their story, as though I had some wisdom to give them, and along about the time they're restating the problem for the third time they tell me what they want to hear; and I always wait a few more paragraphs and then repeat it back to them. And they light right up and go away praising my name. I've gotten used to it."

What do I want to hear? he asked himself, and honestly did not know.

"One man, though . . . once a man came to me who had been engaged to a woman for six years, all through school. They had gotten as far as selecting the wallpaper for the house. And one day she told him she felt a Vocation. God had called her to be a nun." Debbie pulled red hair out from under her collar and swept it back with both hands, glancing at the mirror over a nearby bureau. "He was a devout Catholic himself. By his own rules, *he couldn't even be sad.* He was supposed to rejoice." She rubbed at a lipstick smear near the base of her throat. "There's a word for that, and I'm amazed at how few people know it, because it's the word for the sharpest tragedy a human can feel. 'Antinomy.' It means, 'contradiction between two propositions which seem equally urgent and necessary.'" She retrieved her purse, took out a pack of Reefer and selected one. "I didn't know what in hell's name to tell that man," she said reflectively, and put the joint back in the pack.

Suddenly she turned and confronted him. "I still don't, Bill. *I* don't know which one of you Virginia would pick in a fair contest, and I don't know what it would do to Dr. Higgins if he *were* to lose her to you. A torch that burns for ten years must be awfully hot." She shuddered. "It might just have burned him to a crisp already.

"But you, on the other hand: I would say that you could get over her, more or less completely, in six months. Eight at the outside. If that's what you decide, I'll come back for you in . . . oh, a few weeks. You'll be ready for me then." She smiled gently, and reached out to touch his cheek. "Of course . . . if you do that . . . you'll never know, will you?" And she was gone.

Forty-five minutes later he jumped up and said, "Hey wait!" and then felt very foolish indeed.

Virginia Harding took off her headphones, switched off the stereo and sighed irritably. Ponty's bow had just been starting to really smoke, but the flood of visual imagery it evoked had been so intolerably rich that involuntarily she had opened her eyes — and seen the clock on the far wall. The relaxation period she had allowed herself was over.

Here I sit, she thought, *a major medical miracle, not a week out of the icebox and I'm buried in work. God, I hate money.*

She could, of course, have done almost literally anything she chose; had she requested it, the president of the hospital's board of directors would happily have dropped whatever he was doing and come to stand by her bedside and turn pages for her. But such freedom was too crushing for her to be anything but responsible with it.

Only the poor can afford to goof off. I can't even spare the time for a walk with Bill. Dammit, I still owe him an apology too. She would have enjoyed nothing more than to spend a pleasant hour with the handsome young Orientator, learning how to get along in polite society. But business traditionally came before pleasure, and she had more pressing duties. A fortune such as hers represented the life energy of many many people; as long as it persisted in *being* hers, she meant to take personal responsibility for it. It had been out of her direct control for over a decade, and the very world of finance in which its power inhered had changed markedly in the interim. She was trying to absorb a decade at once — and determined to waste no time. A desk with microviewer and computer-bank inputs had been installed in her hospital room, and the table to the left of it held literally hundreds of microfilm cassettes, arranged by general heading in eight cartons and chronologically within them. The table on the right held the half-carton she had managed to review over the last five days. She had required three one-hour lectures by an earnest, aged specialist-synthesist to understand even that much. She had *expected* to encounter startling degrees and kinds of change, but this was incredible.

Another hour and a half on the Delanier-Garcia Act, she decided, *half an hour of exercise, lunch and those damnable pills, snatch ten minutes to visit Tom and then let the damned medicos poke and prod and test me for the rest of the afternoon. Supper if I've the stomach for any, see Tom again, then back to work. With any luck I'll have 1982 down by the time I fall asleep. God's teeth.*

She was already on her feet, her robe belted and slippers on. She activated the intercom and ordered coffee, crossed the room and sat down at the desk, which began to hum slightly. She heated up the microviewer, put the Silent Steno on standby and was rummaging in the nearest carton for her next tape when a happy thought struck her. Perhaps the last tape in the box would turn out to be a summary. She pulled it out and fed it to the desk, and by God it was — it appeared to be an excellent and thorough summary at that. *Do you suppose*, she asked herself, *that the last tape in the last box would be a complete overview? Would Charlesworthy & Cavanaugh be that thoughtful? Worth a try. God, I need some shortcuts.* She selected that tape and popped the other, setting it aside for later.

The door chimed and opened, admitting one of her nurses — the one whose taste in eyeshadow was abominable. He held a glass that appeared to contain milk and lemon juice half and half with rust flakes stirred in. From across the room it smelled bad.

"I'm sorry," she said gravely. "Even in a hospital you can't tell me that's a cup of coffee."

"Corpuscle paint, Ms. Harding," he said cheerfully. "Doctor's orders."

"Kindly tell the doctor that I would be obliged if he would insert his thumb, rectally, to the extent of the first joint, pick himself up and hold himself at arm's length until I drink that stuff. Advise him to put on an overcoat first, because hell's going to freeze over in the meantime. And speaking of hell, where *in* it is my coffee?"

"I'm sorry, Ms. Harding. No coffee. Stains the paint — you don't want tacky corpuscles."

"*Dammit . . .*"

"Come on, drink it. It doesn't taste as bad as it smells. Quite."

"Couldn't I take it intravenously or something? Oh Christ, give it to me." She drained it in a single gulp and shivered, beating her fists on her desk in revulsion. "God. God. God. Damn. Can't I just have my leukemia back?"

His face sobered. "Ms. Harding — look, it's none of my business, but if I was you, I'd be a little more grateful. You give those lab boys a hard time. You've come back literally from death's door. Why don't you be patient while we make sure it's locked behind you?"

She sat perfectly still for five seconds, and then saw from his face that he thought he had just booted his job out the window. "Oh Manuel, I'm sorry. I'm not angry. I'm ... astounded. You're right, I haven't been very gracious about it all. It's just that, from my point of view, as far as *I* remember, I never *had* leukemia. I guess I resent the doctors for trying to tell me that I ever was that close to dying. I'll try and be a better patient." She made a face. "But God, that stuff tastes ghastly."

He smiled and turned to go, but she called him back. "Would you leave word for Bill McLaughlin that I won't be able to see him until tomorrow after all?"

"He didn't come in today," the nurse said. "But I'll leave word." He left, holding the glass between thumb and forefinger.

She turned back to her desk and inserted the new cassette, but did not start it. Instead she chewed her lip and fretted. *I wonder if I was as blasé the last time. When they told me I had it. Are those memories gone because I want them to be?*

She knew perfectly well that they were not. But anything that reminded her of those missing six months upset her. She could not reasonably regret the bargain she had made, but almost she did. Theft of her memories struck her as the most damnable invasion of privacy, made her very flesh crawl, and it did not help to reflect that it had been done with her knowledge and consent. From her point of view it had not; it had been authorized by another person who had once occupied this body, now deceased, by suicide. A life shackled to great wealth had taught her that her memories were the *only* things uniquely hers, and she mourned them, good, bad or indifferent. Mourned them more than she missed the ten years spent in freeze: she had not *experienced* them.

She had tried repeatedly to pin down exactly what was the last thing she could remember before waking up in the plastic coffin, and had found the task maddeningly difficult. There were half a dozen candidates for last-remembered-day in her memory, none of them conveniently cross-referenced with time and date, and at least one or two of those appeared to be false memories, cryonic dreams. She had the feeling that if she had tried immediately upon awakening, she would have remembered, as you can sometimes remember last night's dream if you try at once. But she had been her usual efficient self, throwing all her energies into adapting to the new situation.

Dammit, I want those memories back! I know I swapped six months for a lifetime, but at that rate it'll be five months and twenty-five days before I'm even breaking even. I think I'd even settle for a record of some kind — if only I'd had the sense to start a diary!

She grimaced in disgust at the lack of foresight of the dead Virginia Harding, and snapped the microviewer on with an angry gesture. And then she dropped her jaw and said, "Jesus Christ in a floater bucket!"

The first frame read, "PERSONAL DIARY OF VIR-GINIA HARDING."

If you have never experienced major surgery, you are probably unfamiliar with the effects of three days of morphine followed by a day of demerol. Rather similar results might be obtained by taking a massive dose of LSD-25 while hopelessly drunk. Part of the consciousness is fragmented . . . and part expanded. Time-sense and durational perception go all to hell, as do coordination, motor skills, and concentration — and yet often the patient, turning inward, makes a quantum leap toward a new plateau of self-understanding and insight. Everything seems suddenly clear: structures of lies crumble, hypocrisies are stripped naked, and years' worth of comfortable rationalizations collapse like cardboard kettles, splashing boiling water everywhere. Perhaps the mind reacts to major shock by reassessing, with ruthless honesty, everything that has brought it there. Even Saint Paul must have been close to something when he found himself on the ground beside his horse, and Higgins had the advantage of being colossally stoned.

While someone ran an absurd stop-start, variable-speed movie in front of his eyes, comprised of doctors and nurses and I.V. bottles and bedpans and blessed pricks on the arm, his mind's eye looked upon himself and pronounced him a fool. His stupidity seemed so massive, so transparent in retrospect that he was filled with neither dismay nor despair, but only with wonder.

My god it's so obvious! *How could I have had my eyes so tightly shut? Choking up like that when they started to Goof, for Christ's sake — do I need a neon sign? I used to have a sense of humor — if there was anything Ginny and I had in common it was a gift for repartee — and after ten years of "selfless dedication" to Ginny and leukemia and keeping the money coming that's exactly what I haven't got any more and I damned well know it. I've shriveled up like a raisin, an ingrown man.*

I've been a zombie for ten mortal years, telling myself that neurotic monomania was a Great And Tragic Love, trying to cry loud enough to get what I wanted. The only friend I made in those whole ten years was Bill, and I didn't hesitate to use him *when I found out our PPs matched. I knew bloody well that I'd grown smaller instead of bigger since she loved me, and he was the perfect excuse for my ego. Play games with his head to avoid overhauling my own. I was going to lose, I knew I was going to lose, and then I was going to accidentally "let slip" the truth to her, and spend the next ten years bathing in someone else's pity than my own. What an incredible, impossible, histrionic fool I've been, like a neurotic child saying, "Well, if you won't give me the candy I'll just smash my hand with a hammer."*

If only I hadn't needed *her so much when I met*

her. Oh, I must find some way to set this right, as quickly as possible!

His eyes clicked into focus, and Virginia Harding was sitting by his bedside in a soft brown robe, smiling warmly. He felt his eyes widen.

"Dilated to see you," he blurted, and giggled.

Her smile disappeared. "Eh?"

"Pardon me. Demerol was first synthesized to wean Hitler off morphine; consequently I'm Germanic-depressive these days." *See? The ability is still there. Dormant, atrophied, but still there.*

The smile returned. "I see you're feeling better."

"How would you know?"

It vanished again. "What are you talking about?"

"I know you're probably quite busy, but I expected a visit before this." *Light, jovial — keep it up, boy.*

"Tom Higgins, I have been here twice a day ever since you got out of OR."

"What?"

"You have conversed with me, lucidly and at length, told me funny stories and discussed contemporary politics with great insight, as far as I can tell. You don't remember."

"Not a bit of it." He shook his head groggily. *What did I say? What did I tell her?* "That's incredible. That's just incredible. You've been here . . ."

"Six times. This is the seventh."

"My God. I wonder where I was. This is appalling."

"Tom, you may not understand me, but I know precisely how you feel."

"Eh?" *That made you jump.* "Oh yes, your missing six months." *Suppose sometime in my lost three days we had agreed to love each other forever — would that still be binding now?* "God, what an odd sensation."

"Yes it is," she agreed, and something in her voice made him glance sharply at her. She flushed and got up from her bedside chair, began to pace around the room. "It might not be so bad if the memories just stayed *completely* gone . . ."

"What do you mean?"

She appeared not to hear the urgency in his voice. "Well, it's nothing I can pin down. I . . . I just started wondering. Wondering why I kept visiting you so regularly. I mean, I like you — but I've been so damned busy I haven't had time to scratch, I've been missing sleep and missing meals, and every time visiting hours opened up I stole ten minutes to come and see you. At first I chalked it off to a not unreasonable feeling that I was in your debt — not just because you defrosted me without spoiling anything, but because you got shot trying to protect me too. There was a rock outcropping right next to you that would have made peachy cover."

"I . . . I . . . " he sputtered.

"That felt right," she went on doggedly, "but not entirely. I felt . . . I *feel* something else for you, something I don't understand. Sometimes when I look at you, there's . . . there's a feeling something like déjà vu, a vague feeling that there's something between us that I don't know. I know it's crazy — you'd surely have told me by now — but did I ever know you? Before?"

There it is, tied up in pink ribbon on a silver

salver. You're a damned fool if you don't reach out and take it. In a few days she'll be out of this mausoleum and back with her friends and acquaintances. Some meddling bastard will tell her sooner or later — do it now, while there's still a chance. You can pull it off: you've seen your error — now that you've got her down off the damn pedestal you can give her a mature love, you can grow tall enough to be a good man for her, you can do it right this time.

All you've got to do is grow ten years' worth overnight.

"Ms. Harding, to the best of my knowledge I never saw you before this week." And that's the damn truth.

She stopped pacing, and her shoulders squared. "I told you it was crazy. I guess I didn't want to admit that all those memories were completely gone. I'll just have to get used to it, I suppose."

"I imagine so." We both will. "Ms. Harding?"

"Yes?"

"Whatever the reasons, I do appreciate your coming to see me, and I'm sorry I don't recall the other visits, but right at the moment my wound is giving me merry hell. Could you come back again, another time? And ask them to send in someone with another shot?"

He failed to notice the eagerness with which she agreed. When she had gone and the door had closed behind her, he sank his face into his hands and wept.

Her desk possessed a destruct unit for the incineration of confidential reports, and she found that it accepted microfilm cassettes. She was just closing the lid when the door chimed and McLaughlin came in, looking a bit haggard. "I hope I'm not intruding," he said.

"Not at all, come in," she said automatically. She pushed the *burn* button, felt the brief burst of heat, and took her hand away. "Come on in, Bill, I'm glad you came."

"They gave me your message, but I . . ." He appeared to be searching for words.

"No, really, I changed my plans. Are you on call tonight, Bill? Or otherwise occupied?"

He looked startled "No."

"I intended to spend the night reading these damned reports, but all of a sudden I feel an overwhelming urge to get stinking drunk with someone — no." She caught herself and looked closely at him, seemed to see him as though for the first time. "No, by God, to get stinking drunk with *you*. Are you willing?"

He hesitated for a long time.

"I'll go out and get a bottle," he said at last.

"There's one in the closet. Bourbon okay?"

Higgins was about cried out when his own door chimed. Even so, he nearly decided to feign sleep, but at the last moment he sighed, wiped his face with his sleeves, and called out, "Come in."

The door opened to admit a young nurse with high cheeks, soft lips, vivid red hair and improbably gray eyes.

"Hello, nurse," he said. He did not know her either. "I'm afraid I need something for pain."

"I know," she said softly, and moved closer. •

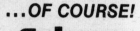

GOOD-BY TO ALL THAT

by Frederik Pohl

Photo by Jay Kay Klein

The other day my contract as Bantam Book's science-fiction editor ran out and I declined to renew it. I'll still continue to ride herd on a few special projects, but that's it. Nothing new. (For any reader who may wish to submit to Bantam, Ms. Sydny Weinberg is the person to submit to.) I started editing science fiction with *Astonishing Stories* in 1939, so that makes thirty-nine years of doing it, and that's really enough.

But the decision to hang up my blue pencil (actually, these days it's a red Flair) makes me philosophical, and I'd like to talk about the theory and practice of editing.

What is an editor?

The best answer I know is an old novel called *Friends of Mr Sweeny*, by Elmer Davis. It's long out

Good-by to All that

of print, and I haven't read it for dozens of years, but as near as I can remember it says, "An editor is a man who can explain dam design to an archeologist and Egyptian burial customs to a hydraulics engineer." An editor is a middleman. He squeezes enough money out of the publisher to keep the writers going, and secures good enough work from the writer to turn a profit for the publisher. He conveys to the readers what the writers are trying to do, and explains to the writers what the readers will sit still for. He doesn't have to know science, but he has to be able to tell if a writer does. He doesn't have to have the creative or literary skills of a writer, but he has to be able to maximize them in his contributors. Those are minima. If he is good, he can be more—oh, much more—than that.

Science fiction owes more to its editors than any other branch of literature, and this is a curious thing. Who knows who Mark Twain's editor was? Or, for that matter, Joseph Heller's or Jacqueline Suzanne's? But the names of John Campbell, Tony Boucher and Horace Gold are mighty in sf. Even members of the Mystery Writers of America might have trouble identifying Cap Shaw or Daisy Bacon, but what SFWA member is ignorant of Hugo Gernsback?

The *best* science-fiction editors—so say I, anyway—knew sf before they began editing it. Campbell, Gernsback, Gold, Bova and Boucher wrote it. Hornig, Scithers, and Wollheim were fans. McComas had been an anthologist; Mills had been associated with sf publishing in other capacities before taking over as editor.

Contrariwise, the worst sf editors are the ones

who never had any interest in science fiction until someone told them to. Now, there are a few honorable exceptions. Judy-Lynn del Ray had no idea there was such a thing as science fiction before she came aboard as my assistant at *Galaxy* in the mid-60s—and what a powerhouse she is! Betty Ballantine, almost the same. F. Orlin Tremaine had it even tougher; he became Street & Smith's editor of *Astounding* because Management pointed at him and said, "You're it"—and he didn't even have the example of an earlier savvy sf editor to learn from, because there had hardly been any. But how rare these exceptions are!

Over the past fifty years there have been close to five hundred editors charged with buying or bouncing science fiction for American publishers. Maybe twenty-five, tops, have been really standout good at it. Perhaps another fifty, pretty good; and fifty more have had the ability, but the publisher wouldn't pay or the magazine folded or the books were badly produced—endless are the hazards that can destroy an editor's work—and so it went for naught.

The other three hundred and seventy-five?

Well. . . .A lot of them were nice people. A quality which, along with ten pennies, will get you a dime.

Your average everyday science-fiction editor of the present is usually young, generally possessed of a brand-new bachelor's degree in English Lit. and more often than not female. None of these qualities disqualify her—or him. But they don't do diddly-squat to qualify him, either. The best thing you can say about them is that they are irrelevant to being any good as a science-fiction editor—and yet there, over and over, they are. If we are lucky, sometimes he (or she) has at least read science fiction at one time, and that's cool. He might still be lousy as an editor, but at least he's got the tools to work with.

But all too often he has not. Of the ones who know nothing about sf, some are tragically unaware of their ignorance; they've seen *Star Wars* and read *Chariots of the Gods*, and what else do they need? God help them—and us. Some do know how little they know. So first day on the job they call up someone who they think can explain it to them in ninety minutes. They take him to lunch, and they do what he says. Or what they retain of what he says. Or what they have understood of what they retain of what he says. That system can break down at every point, but where it goes most terribly wrong is in selecting the brain to pick; oh, brethren, what flakes have laid down laws that bound us all!

Now, if there were a God in Heaven it is certain the He would smite these sinners with the scourge of Returns and the pestilence of Losses. Perhaps He is busy elsewhere. I do believe, as a matter of faith, that there is some rough justice in the world and that, statistically speaking, good books on the whole will perform better than bad ones. But that's faith speaking, not evidence. The evidence is less sure. Production values count. Hype works. Management orders get followed. The book that is so bad that it cannot somehow be inflated into some sort of success has not yet been written, and many a sinner has prospered a *lot*.

I don't mean that it is easy to jump up a dog into a best-seller. It isn't. It takes money, and effort, and resourcefulness, and even then it doesn't always work. (Thank God.) But there are powerful strategies available to those willing to use them. Window displays. Space ads. TV spot commercials. The more effective they are the more they cost, and sometimes they cost more than they're worth. Still, if you put a million dollars into TV spots you are going to sell a million books—regardless, or anyway *almost* regardless, of what the book is. If a top editor, with both muscle and credibility, tells the annual sales meeting that they'll sell 60,000 copies of this here hardbound, then they will. (At the cost, maybe, of selling 60,000 less of something else.) One very large hard-cover company used to be in bed with one very large bookstore chain. The salesmen used to get a secret cash bonus for every copy of that publisher's book they sold. Until anti-trust made them stop, it was *impossible* for that publisher to bring out a book that lost. Other publishers discounted books—take a nickel a copy less than the big boys charge. That makes a significant difference to an outlet that moves a hundred thousand books a week. In the bad old days, sometimes that nickel went under the table to the buyer for the chain—and, boy, did *that* make a difference! (Now you know why your local Mafia numbers front used to have all those copies of *Squalid Sex-Goddesses of Sigma Lyrae* and so little of Clarke or Heinlein.)

I've been talking about exceptional promotion methods, and even a few sort of illegal ones. But there are many that are legal and even customary, and when they are put to work they make books move. And it's not just promotion. If you can scheme a way to save a penny or two on printing each copy—*or* attract advertising or some other revenue—or tie in with a red-hot TV or movie project—*or* find a cover or a blurb that works—*or* do any of a hundred other things, you can move a book that will just lie there on its own. Oh, it's certainly a real plus factor if an editor can tell the difference between a good story and a bad one. But even if he can't, he can survive—and if he can, he can prosper—if he can get the other factors working for him.

To succeed as an editor, you must get your hands on the levers of power:

To make the machine go. To bully, bribe or sweet-talk the sales people and the promotion people and all the other people in the place so that they do all the things they should do anyway, but won't.

To change the machine's programming. Schedules, prices, contract terms, formats are not ordained by God, only by Management. When Management's wrong, it is an act of loyalty to straighten them out. (Although they don't always see it that way.)

And, having done all that, you can then think about that third and most pleasurable lever to work:

To introduce the person into the machine. To so interact with the writers, the people that publishing is all about, to produce words that entertain, enlighten, stimulate, inspire and/or delight the reader. And you.

What gives an editor the right to tell an author how his story should be written? John Campbell used to defuse that charge by saying, "Look, Fred." (Or Isaac, or Doc, or Bob.) "You know more about yourself than I ever will, but there's one part of you that I know better than you do. That's the back of your neck. I can see it, and you can't; and it's the same with this story." and, as so often, John's quirky logic was pretty much right. A writer can get so wrapped up in his story that he cannot see forest for trees.

I know this is so for me, as writer. So I make it a practice to let the rough draft of anything I write cool for a while—a week, a month, sometimes a matter of years—until I have forgotten enough of it to see it with fresh eyes, before I do the final draft. Even so, editors like Horace Gold have often brought me up standing by seeing something on the back of my own story's neck that was hidden from me. And that external view is what an editor can give to a writer that the writer can't always give himself.

And, oh, what fun to play God! That is the aspect of editing that sucks the English Lit. graduates out of Wellesley and Northwestern into the publishing world of Madison and Fifth. It was what hooked John Campbell for thirty-four years, so that he died still an addict. It's an ego trip.

It's also an opportunity to do something worth doing. Forgive me if this part sounds like vanity. It probably is; but it's worth doing, to find ways to bring to an audience good things they might not otherwise have. I've been talking about this at some length in my autobiography, *The Way the Future Was*, upcoming shortly in hard-cover at your favorite book store. But the autobiography stops about the time I stopped editing magazines—because events after that are still too close for me to make enough sense of them to write about them—and there are things that strike me as rewarding about editing books, too.

Of course, what I call "doing something worth while" you might easily call my "ego trip", because a lot depends, doesn't it, on what we each define as "worth while". But there's pleasure in publishing Delany's *Dhalgren*, after a dozen other editors have declared it unmarketable, and seeing it go through twelve large printings; in taking the gamble with a new writer like Janet Morris, committing to four long novels before one customer anywhere has bought one word of hers in print, and seeing *The High Couch of Silistra* build her an audience; in seeing a book where even the author hasn't seen it yet—as in the upcoming *Medea: Harlan's World*—and making it happen. There is a novel not yet published, and not science-fiction, either, by a writer named Gustav Hasford. It is about the Vietnam war, and it is scarifying. I don't promise you will like it, but I promise you will never forget it; and when I came across it,, quite by chance, the author had had a string of rejections from people who said, "Jesus, this is *remarkable*, but I don't see it as a commercial possibility." Well, maybe it isn't. But there is a religious question involved here. It is my religious belief that a voice that has something new and insightful to say about the world deserves to be heard; it is the publishing industry's responsibility to provide a forum for that hearing, and if it fails to do so it betrays its trust. So I went to bat, and Hasford is going to be heard at last, and I take delight in that I made it happen. Or made it happen now, anyway; because the other part of my religion states that if something is worth being heard, sooner or later some editor and publisher will give it birth. Hasford would not have been muted forever. As I've said, I think in the long run injustices even out. (But the trouble with the long run, as John Maynard Keynes told Franklin D. Roosevelt, is that in the long run we are all dead.) It is an editor's privilege—and it is bloody well his duty, too—to repair some of the injustices while the author is still able to enjoy it.

So much for vanity . . . and maybe more than enough.

While I was writing this article, I had occasion to glance through an essay I had written called *The Publishing of Science Fiction*. (It's in a book called *Science Fiction Today and Tomorrow*, edited by Reginald Bretnor.) I wrote it only half a dozen years ago, but already the numbers are all wrong. I spoke of the average hard-cover sf novel price as maybe $4.95, and of a typical author's advance as around $2,000.

There's not much of that around any more. Not long ago a science-fiction novel went up for paperback auction, and in the bidding that followed it sold for around a quarter of a million dollars. That's an interesting number, in a lot of ways. The most interesting thing about it is that I did a little arithmetic, and it turns out that the aggregate amount I paid out as an editor to everybody, over a period of thirty years from 1939 to 1969, as editor of *Astonishing Stories* and *Super Science Stories*, as editor of the *Star* series of original anthologies for Ballantine, as editor of more than a dozen reprint anthologies over that period and finally as editor of *Galaxy*, *If*, *Worlds of Tomorrow* and others for nearly a decade—the total of checks for all of them put together, to every contributor, is probably just about that same quarter of a million.

A quarter of a million dollars is surely a high price to pay for a science-fiction book, even now. But it is not unique. There are books that have earned more. Sure, there's inflation to consider. The 1939 dollar was worth maybe ten times the present's in purchasing power. But if inflation has increased the numbers in everything by a factor of ten, it is also true that the earnings for science fiction have gone up by a factor of maybe a hundred. Science fiction used to have an occasional drift-in of writers who couldn't get published in any other field, and though maybe they could make it in science fiction. Now the drift-in is of writers who can get published in other fields, all right, but can't live on it. They think science fiction will be more lucrative, and sometimes they're right.

One reason for this escalation is the paperback auction I mentioned a moment ago. Most people don't know how that works—even many writers don't. It goes something like this. Some hard-cover publisher buys a science-fiction novel. They set it in type and print up sets of bound proofs, looking like a rather sloppy actual book, and send them around to the major paperback science-fiction editors: Jim Baen at Ace, Nancy Neiman at Avon, Judy-Lynn del Rey at Ballantine-Del Rey, Sydny Weinberg (or until recently me) at Bantam, Don Wollheim at DAW-NAL, Adele Hull at Jove, Dave Hartwell at Pocket, maybe one or two others. If they are confident, they set a date for an auction. If they're not, they wait for the phone to ring. Then, if somebody shows an interest in acquiring the right to publish that book in a paperback edition, they call around to the other editors to see if there's any competition, and if so *then* they set an auction date.

Considering the large appetitie for such goods on the part of the paperback publishers, it's surprising to say that there are a fair number of hard-cover science-fiction books published that no paperback editor wants to bid on. (Although, considering the quality of some of them, maybe it's not only not surprising, but even encouraging.) Once the auction starts, the phones run hot. "I've got thirty-five thousand, will you go for forty?" "Can I pre-empt right now for sixty-five?" The numbers may be larger, and they're often a lot smaller, but the auction is the name of the game.

All this is exciting, in a heady, heavy-pressure way, and it certainly has enriched a lot of us. Once the bidding fever starts, it carries publishers heaven knows where. But it is more like speculating on wheat futures than it is like Maxwell Perkins patiently going over line by line of Thomas Wolfe, or like John Campbell, endlessly firing off polemics and challenges, and chortling over the stories that came back. It is an interesting game to play. But so is Monopoly, and Monopoly, at least, does not distort one's values.

The really best thing there is about helping to create science fiction, whether as a writer or as an editor, is painting pictures no one has ever seen, stimulating thoughts that the reader might not otherwise ever have thought, suggesting concerns and delights that might not otherwise have occurred to anyone.

An editor can play a big part in that, but not as big as a writer can. And so at last, perhaps a little tardily, I've made up my mind. That's what I want to be when I grow up: a writer.   ●

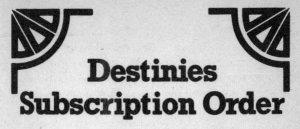

Destinies
Subscription Order

Name _____

Street _____

City or Town _____

State & Zip _____

Enclosed find my check or money order, made out to BOOK MAILING SERVICE, for $13.50. The next six issues of <u>DESTINIES</u> will be sent to me on publication.

Please send subscription orders to:

**BOOK MAILING SERVICE
ACE SCIENCE FICTION DIVISION
BOX 650
ROCKVILLE CENTRE, N.Y. 11571**

And, as an introductory offer to new subscribers, all purchase orders for any Ace Science Fiction titles (including back issues of <u>DESTINIES</u>) which accompany a <u>DESTINIES</u> subscription will be shipped free of postage and handling charges (up to $1.50 in savings). These offers are subject to withdrawal or change without notice.